MODERN AMERICAN ENGINEERS

LIPPINCOTT BOOKS BY EDNA YOST:

AMERICAN WOMEN OF SCIENCE
AMERICAN WOMEN OF NURSING
MODERN AMERICANS IN SCIENCE AND INVENTION

□□□□□□□□□□□□□□□□□□□□□□□□□□□□

MODERN
AMERICAN
ENGINEERS

By Edna Yost

J. B. LIPPINCOTT COMPANY
PHILADELPHIA & NEW YORK

For

L. M. G.

Preface

IN THIS BOOK I have aimed to give a partial picture of modern engineers through life stories of a dozen engineers. Out of many specialized fields of engineering I selected, with the help of my publisher, a dozen fields of wide interest. Some of the omissions—highway engineering, for example, or chemical engineering, metallurgical engineering, heating and ventilating engineering, and others—were hard to make. But space limitations made omissions necessary. In some cases decisions on fields to be omitted were easier to make because they had already been included in my earlier book, *Modern Americans in Science and Invention.*

When decision had been reached on the fields to be included in the present book, I made my selection, with thoughtful help from the staffs of various national engineering societies, and others qualified to give advice, of a man of high achievement in each of the chosen fields, and secured his consent and promise of cooperation. Because professional groups have responsibility, in a democracy, for a share of leadership in community and national life, in the group selected were several men who had gone on from achievement in engineering to occupy places of leadership in public affairs.

As in my three earlier books of biographical sketches, no attempt was made to select the greatest man in his specialized field of work. Each was chosen as an engineer recognized by his peers as a man of high achievement. They turned out to be a splendid group to work with, and I wish to express here, as I have to each of them personally, my appreciation for their time and help in supplying facts and directing me toward further facts of their lifework. I want to state, too, that their consent and cooperation were not secured until they were convinced that the book I had in mind met a genuine need in the educational world.

Drama struck suddenly as the book was in its initial stages. Three days after my interview with Dr. Robert E. Doherty, in the offices of the Carnegie Foundation for Peace in New York City, Dr. Doherty died. I will always wonder if he may not have had premonition of his going, for he reviewed his life for me that afternoon with a clarity and completeness I had never met before—the kind of clarity, I found myself thinking three days later, with which a drowning man is said to see his whole life in an instant of time. Especial thanks are due Dr. Doherty's friend and co-worker, Dr. Elliott Dunlap Smith, Provost of Carnegie Institute of Technology, for the generosity and adequacy of his efforts in supplying facts, and then in giving the manuscript the careful checking Dr. Doherty had intended to do himself when we parted.

Some may wonder at the omission of Herbert Hoover's name in the list I have chosen. Decision not to approach Mr. Hoover was made because of the wealth of biographical material already available on this perhaps best known of all American engineers.

Edna Yost

Contents

                                                    PAGE

1   ROBERT ERNEST DOHERTY

Engineering Educator, whose "Carnegie Plan" for engineering education grew out of a personal experience of twenty-two years in industry   1

2   RALPH EDWARD FLANDERS

Mechanical Engineer, whose experience in designing machines has served him well in the United States Senate   17

3   ARTHUR ERNEST MORGAN

Civil Engineer, specialist in flood-control work, former chairman of TVA, originator of Antioch's Work and Study Program, believer in the small community as the foundation of democratic life   32

4   VANNEVAR BUSH

Electrical Engineer, inventor of a "Mechanical Brain," who as wartime director of our national scientific research contributed to America's early success in the use of atomic energy   47

5   SCOTT TURNER

Mining Engineer, ex-Director of the United States Bureau of Mines, who directed the first commercial coal mining within the Arctic Circle   60

6   J. BROWNLEE DAVIDSON

Who saw the need for greater application of engineering methods to farm problems, and pioneered in creating the profession of *Agricultural Engineering*   77

7   HAROLD BRIGHT MAYNARD
     Industrial Engineering Consultant, President
     of the Methods Engineering Council, which
     specializes on management problems in industry   91

8   OLE SINGSTAD
     Norwegian-born and Norwegian-educated
     American *Civil Engineer*, designer of the
     Holland Tunnel and its ventilating system,
     who became the world's greatest authority on
     vehicular tunnels   107

9   JOHN ROBERT SUMAN
     Petroleum Engineer, whose work has been
     greatly responsible for doubling the amount
     of oil recovered from earth's hidden reservoirs   122

10   CARL GEORGE ARTHUR ROSEN
     Research Engineer, who invented fuel-injection equipment which put the Diesel Engine
     on the production line   140

11   STANWOOD WILLSTON SPARROW
     Automotive Engineer, who has contributed
     to better airplanes in time of war and better
     automobiles in time of peace   155

12   HAROLD ALDEN WHEELER
     Radio and Television Engineer, whose teenage invention helped finance his college education, and whose later inventions helped win
     World War II   168

◻◻◻◻◻◻◻◻ 1 ◻◻◻◻◻◻◻◻

Robert Ernest Doherty

(1885 — 1950)

ENGINEERING EDUCATOR, WHOSE "CAR-
NEGIE PLAN" FOR ENGINEERING EDUCATION
GREW OUT OF A PERSONAL EXPERIENCE OF
TWENTY-TWO YEARS IN INDUSTRY

◻◻◻◻◻◻◻◻◻◻◻◻◻◻◻◻◻◻◻◻◻◻◻◻◻◻◻

WHEN the engineer who
became President of Carnegie Institute of Technology in
1936 was graduated from college he had, he said, a "vague
notion" about some of his inadequacies. Within him was a
hazy realization that he did not completely understand the
principles beneath some of the engineering routines and
techniques he had learned. This vague notion about his
inadequacies became a conviction during his early years in
industry. Here he found he could not solve many of the
problems a young engineer must meet. Yet, often when
a superior showed him the way out of his dilemma, Bob
Doherty recognized that he already knew the principles
upon which the solution had been based, but had somehow
failed to recognize their bearing upon his problem.

Contact with scores of other young engineers at General
Electric, and later with hundreds of them, soon convinced

him that he shared his inadequacies with graduates of every engineering school in the country. Everywhere student engineers had had their heads filled with facts and their hands trained to techniques. But they did not have the training which would enable them to think successfully through a new form of technical problem based upon the very principles they could quote so glibly from memory.

Because something grew out of that conviction, Robert Doherty's life has written one of the most important chapters in the history of modern professional education. There are still institutions able to call themselves engineering schools where the curriculum is more conducive to training technicians than to educating engineers. There are many schools today in which an understanding of the principles beneath technological facts and routines is stressed, and in which ability to apply these principles to new problems is developed. But at Carnegie Tech, Robert Doherty set about creating a curriculum which goes beyond that advanced step in engineering education. It was his conviction that professional groups should furnish leadership in human affairs, and that engineers should be as responsible as lawyers, doctors, or other professional groups for supplying such citizen leadership. The curriculum he instituted at the Engineering School of Carnegie Institute of Technology combines fundamental education in engineering principles and the art of using them with education which simultaneously attempts to develop a student's full human capacities and awaken him to his responsibilities as a potential leader in human affairs. The young man or woman thinking of engineering as a lifework today has opportunity for these three types of educational preparation.

Bob Doherty's boyhood was like that of thousands of other boys in the Middle West in the last decades of the nineteenth century. With his father, mother, and six brothers and sisters he grew up in Clay City, Illinois, a rural community containing little stimulation to higher education. Its high school gave a boy a diploma without fitting him for entrance to the State University. Despite its impressive name Clay City had only a few hundred inhabitants, and neither electric lights nor telegraph office when Bob was born. Maybe the fact that he was old enough to be impressed by the first electric lights in his community, and to be excited by the arrival of its first telegraph office gave a dramatic importance to electricity which it would not have for later generations who never knew a world without such things. At any rate, by the time he was in high school Bob Doherty felt a greater pull toward the telegraph office in the Baltimore and Ohio Station than toward his father's drugstore. He knew instinctively he wanted to be an engineer and specialize in electricity.

By the time he had reached high school he was building his own successful telegraph instruments at home, as multitudes of boys of a later generation would be building radio sets. First his homemade instruments sent messages from upstairs to downstairs in his own home. Then they communicated over a private wire he and a school friend set up between their homes. The boys could understand the simple messages they signaled each other, but one of them was not satisfied to remain an amateur operator. Bob formed the habit of being in the station near train time, when telegraph messages had to be sent, so he could study the dots and dashes he heard. He made a regular practice of going down for the midnight train because the station-agent-operator was not as busy then as at daytime train times. Often he got up in the middle of the night to go down for the train that passed through Clay City at 3 A.M. He made friends with the station agent and, in exchange for sweeping out the station and the performance of other chores, received instruction in the Morse Code. It was this training which enabled him, after high school graduation, to take a job with the B. and O. as a telegraph operator, salary forty-five dollars per month for a twelve-hour night shift.

A job in this period of his life was very necessary if Bob Doherty was to realize his ambition to become an engineer. Higher education was respected and encouraged in his home. His father had been a teacher before he became a druggist, and four of the seven young Dohertys would go to college eventually. But at this period of their lives family finances were limited. A year or more of preparatory education would have to be financed before Bob could enter the State University. He worked and saved what he could. But he was twenty-one years old before he was able to register as a freshman at the University of Illinois, aiming at a B.S. degree in electrical engineering.

During that freshman year, and without any warning, one of the truly great events of Bob Doherty's life happened. Charles Steinmetz, electrical wizard from Schenectady, was scheduled to address the students on a subject of interest to future electrical engineers. Bob went to the lecture; he listened intently and, by his own admission, he did not understand a word the brilliant, physically misshapen gnome of a man said. Yet something from Charles Steinmetz communicated itself across a sea of student heads that day in a way that marked the whole course of the younger man's life.

"Something about Steinmetz set me on fire," he said. "It was something that had never happened to me before. He set me on fire so truly that from the first moment of seeing and hearing him I was hell-bent on getting to Schenectady and to Steinmetz."

Came 1909 and his graduation and Doherty headed for General Electric's Schenectady plant to work, as have so many thousands of young men, as a test engineer. He spent his days in overalls, down in the dirt, often, looking under and all around a new piece of machinery that was not operating smoothly, trying to figure out what "the bugs" were which were hindering operation, and how to get them out. The very first Saturday afternoon he was in Schenectady he made inquiry from an older employee and went out to see where Dr. Steinmetz lived.

"I wanted to look at the house," he said. "I was still so fired by him I just had to see the house he lived in."

The following Saturday afternoon he went again. This time he knocked at the door. "I was so excited *I just had to see him*. Maybe it took a lot of brass but I had to do it. When he came to the door I told him I wanted to ask him some questions about problems I had met up with in my reading and study."

What Robert Doherty did not know that afternoon was that Dr. Steinmetz was glad to be approached by younger engineers who were genuinely interested in learning how to solve baffling problems by using their own intelligence. So the younger engineer was greatly relieved when the older engineer took the intrusion in a kindly manner and answered all the questions put to him. He was decidedly chagrined, however, when the older man, in turn, asked him some questions he could not answer at all. Still, he was encouraged enough to make a bold suggestion.

"It would be wonderful for me if I could come out and talk with you every once in a while," he said as he was leaving.

"Fine. Come any time at all," Steinmetz replied. "If I'm busy you can go back."

Every Saturday afternoon for years Robert Doherty went back—every Saturday up until the time he had earned advancement to a position which gave him ready access to Dr. Steinmetz during work hours. At the end of those years Doherty could count on the fingers of his two hands the times Dr. Steinmetz had been too busy to see him.

The problems he took with him during those years always, after that first Saturday when he had presented his own problems, pertained to his work at General Electric. Soon many of them dealt with the design of synchronous motors and generators. After his year as a test engineer was over he had been assigned to the Company's engineering office as a design engineer, and gave much of his time to this line of work. Alternating current machinery was then in an early period of its development and Doherty was baffled time and again with the problems it presented. Dr. Steinmetz would always point the way out of his difficulties.

"He did not tell me any new fact," Doherty said. "He pointed out a principle of physics which, if applied to the problem at hand, would tell me what I wanted to know. Then he applied it, and he always made full use of mathematics. Now I already knew the principle. I could recite it. By this time I sometimes even understood it. What I did not understand was that it would help me solve this specific problem. The simple fact is, I had not yet learned to analyze the situation I was meeting in terms of the general principles. Rather, I was looking for a formula and there was no formula. A general principle, or concept, was all that could help me."

Finally Bob Doherty began to be ashamed to "face the music," as he called those sessions in which Dr. Steinmetz pointed out to him a principle he already knew but had not learned to use. A curious thing happened then.

"When I got stuck I began to ask myself how Dr. Steinmetz would look at the situation. This happened not once but time after time. Gradually I began to stand on my own mental feet. Repeated exposure to the discipline of

Steinmetz' mind taught me, within my own mind's limits, how to think about a problem."

Meanwhile, the great Schenectady wizard had begun to pass some of his problems along to Doherty. "I gobbled that up," he said, "and soon the time came when I was spending so much time on Dr. Steinmetz' problems that I suggested to him that I go into his office instead of remaining in the office to which I had been assigned."

Steinmetz agreed heartily with the suggestion, as did G.E. officials. Mr. Doherty was appointed assistant to Dr. Steinmetz in 1918, a post he kept till Steinmetz' death in 1923, when, as a consulting engineer, he inherited his old chief's office.

During the period of his association with Dr. Steinmetz, and later, Mr. Doherty published some important technical papers. They dealt with synchronous motors and other synchronous apparatus, exciter instability, and other phases of work which was rapidly bringing our high-tension electrical systems to the adequacy with which the world is now familiar. They described work which was not only producing practical results in increasing the adequacy of electrical transmission, but work which had extended the whole theory of alternating current machinery. Recognition for his work was accorded him, and recognition usually stimulates a man like Doherty to further effort in the line in which recognition is being won. But in this period Mr. Doherty had been experiencing a type of relationship with other human beings which carried him inevitably toward a professor's chair.

The impetus to a new field of work came primarily through contact with thousands of graduate engineers who were bringing their problems to his desk as he had once taken his problems to Steinmetz. He soon learned that not just a few schools were failing to train students to analyze problems "under their own steam" and think them through scientifically in terms of principle, but that all engineering schools were failing. It seemed to Mr. Doherty that student engineers ought to find in their engineering colleges the type of education that trained them to analyze and think, and the challenge to create such a curriculum became dominant within him. In short, Robert Doherty was on fire again and the flame now pointed away from industry toward a college professorship.

Teaching opportunities came, for engineering colleges were on the lookout for engineer-teachers who had had experience in industry. But Dr. Steinmetz said "No" and General Electric officials said "No" to every suggestion Mr. Doherty made about leaving. They all assured him he would make a mistake if he left industry for college teaching. Doherty turned down several offers but insisted that nevertheless he was going to do for young engineers what could not be done except through teaching. Knowing he would do what he said he would do, the group at General Electric finally said, "Very well. If you *must* teach, do it here," and permitted him to set up a three-year program called "The Advanced Course in Engineering" which was given one full morning a week to a selected group of General Electric's engineers.

The first year (1922) twenty-four men were selected from about five hundred engineers, and Doherty began the development of a course designed to teach engineers how to think scientifically and creatively about any problem met in their daily work—and with plenty of mathematics, as Steinmetz had always insisted. As Doherty himself had once learned this way of thinking, he now tried to teach young men to analyze the facts of a baffling problem so that they might recognize the principle upon which solution to the problem depended, and then discover a basis for solving it. Every Saturday morning they came, bringing their problems with them. Doherty knew that if this carefully selected group learned the proper way to approach and think through a few problems they could apply the method successfully to all problems.

At the end of the first year ten of the twenty-four were selected to continue for the next two years of the course, and a new group, this time of thirty-five, selected to enroll for the first year's work. Soon the results were what might be expected from a man like Doherty when he was inspired with an idea, especially in the realm of teaching in which he was truly superb. In scores of young men talents were developed which the Company recognized as far too valuable to be wasted on jobs where they did not have scope. Mr. Doherty's job became more and more a personnel job. He discovered the young men of exceptional talent through his teaching, and then not only had to find the right spot for their special talents but, as he described it, "pick up the apples from apple carts knocked over in those spots." For personality problems often arise when a man of superior technical talents is assigned to some knotty old problem and institutes new methods in order to untie the knots. Mr. Doherty still retained interest in some of his own researches, but eventually he found himself spending most of his time, apart from his conduct of the Advanced Course, acting as assistant to the vice-president in charge of all personnel problems.

Then 1930 arrived, and already the depression was taking serious toll in Schenectady in engineers dismissed. A desk handling personnel problems is never a creative spot at such a time and Mr. Doherty's job lacked satisfactions it had once held. So when Yale University offered him a professorship in electrical engineering, he accepted it.

To leave a good job promising advancement in industry for one in the lower-salaried educational world seemed a great mistake to many people. Measured by the standards

Robert Doherty himself cherished, university teaching offered more than industry. Yet he found himself unhappy
about leaving Dr. Steinmetz' office which he had kept as
it was when his friend had left it. The man who had taught
him how to think held a warm place in his heart. So he
suggested, and General Electric agreed, that the old desk
and blackboard should go to Yale with him. It was a matter of genuine regret to Dr. Doherty later that he had to
be separated from that beloved old desk and blackboard
when he went to Carnegie Tech.

At the Engineering School at Yale, where he became
Dean in another year, Doherty started out to develop the
sort of analytical education Steinmetz had given him. In
addition, he immediately attacked one phase of what may
be one of the most important problems facing Americans
today—the problem of creating an educational system that
develops whole men and women. This was something that
went beyond what he caught from Steinmetz. Doherty
himself had long been living a full human life. A good
citizen in his community of Scotia, outside Schenectady, he
had served for one period as its mayor and for a longer
period on its school board. A warmly human man at home,
he was helping inculcate in his children high moral, aes-
thetic, and spiritual ideals as he and Mrs. Doherty guided
their development. His own marked gift in art was developed through his interest in developing his artist daughter's
gifts. In his professional life he had contributed to technological advancement without diminution of his understanding and handling of the human problems in engineering.
Now he would attempt to create at Yale a spot in the educational world in which engineering students would learn
how to think for themselves in engineering problems and
do it by methods which could be applied to thinking about
other kinds of problems—history, economics, public school
education, or community relationships.

To accomplish both these things takes time. To get time for both it was necessary for students to learn fewer engineering facts and to focus more deeply on a more limited number of engineering subjects than was customary in engineering curricula. Dr. Doherty therefore had to convince authorities at Yale to drop courses at a time when increasing technical knowledge was creating demand for new courses. Faculty members from other departments agreed to cooperate by giving guidance to Doherty's students. But when he tried to have his students apply the scientific method to fields outside their own, he found they had little desire to think at all about anything but engineering! Finally a few students agreed to work on a subject outside their own field. Only one of them carried the project through, that first year, for credit toward a degree.

Because educational projects involve the development of people rather than the changing of things, they are slow in coming to fruition. But each year the fruits showed a little more clearly the validity of Doherty's ideas. At the end of his five years at Yale two unique courses were established in the Electrical Engineering curriculum. The first course used methods for training students to think problems through "under their own steam" which had proved successful at General Electric. The second, far from pertaining to electricity, was taught by a professor with a Ph.D. in history, loaned to the Engineering School. In it each student made a full-scale investigation of some humanistic or social problem in which he had a special interest, wrote it up and presented it to fellow students and faculty. Some students, at least, were accepting the idea that, since their professional life would not be lived in a vacuum, their education should take account of the environment in which their profession would be practiced. Obviously, a wider knowledge of history and economics could fit them better for top-policy-making jobs in the industrial world where engineers were not yet achieving their full share of responsibility. In 1936, at the age of fifty-one, the great opportunity came for which the whole of Dr. Doherty's experience had been fitting him. He became President of Carnegie Institute of Technology in Pittsburgh, with its Schools not only of Engineering and Science but of Fine Arts and Applied Arts. From a president's chair, and in complete charge of all aspects of engineering education, he had an opportunity he had not had before in guiding a whole educational process toward the fulfillment of his vision. Gradually he built up a faculty interested in making his vision a reality. As the faculty grew stronger and worked together longer, taking active part in the planning as well as in the teaching, it became difficult to tell which part of the plans came from Doherty and what came from his associates. But he was the originator, the inspirer, the leader of it all. It was he who got faculty members in different fields to pull together—engineers with historians, English teachers with mathematicians. Gradually the vision became clearer and fuller. As it did it became known as the "Carnegie Plan."

The essence of this plan is its emphasis upon developing in students the character and ability to think self-reliantly and well, throughout their lives and upon all their problems. "The crucial thing," Dr. Doherty said, "is: on which of the two is primary emphasis to be laid—on thinking or on subject matter and techniques?" He answered the question unequivocally, "It should be on the thinking process," and this is the core of the Carnegie Plan. It revolves around his conviction that *college students can be taught how to think so that they can learn for themselves.* If they master this technique of thinking, learning can be a continuous process when classrooms are left behind, and human beings will be equipped to keep up with a changing world, enabled to understand and control it intelligently.

"Root knowledge is what students need," said Doherty,

"not mass cramming of facts. Teach fundamental principles," he urged his faculty. "Teach young people how to analyze situations and use fundamental principles—how to work from root knowledge." So teachers became coaches training students to become thinkers.

"Take the initiative and learn to use your heads," he urged students. "Dig yourself out of confusion. Insist on understanding! Stop memorizing words and formulas you don't understand, merely for a grade. Don't go on cultivating a habit that will cripple your mind for the rest of your days—the habit of superficiality, the habit of accepting confusion as a normal state of mind. You know when you understand and when you don't! With all the emphasis in me I repeat: Insist on thoroughness of understanding."

He saw so clearly, too, that engineering students taught to think about human, social and engineering problems would always have an advantage over those taught to think more narrowly in the technical field only. "The problems of any professional group," he said "have human, economic, social and spiritual as well as technical aspects." So at Carnegie Tech he and his coaching faculty built a program to prepare future engineers to handle these human, economic, social and spiritual aspects of a professional group's problems, and to live as responsible citizens in a free society. This program, a vital part of the Carnegie Plan, consisted of courses in human and social relationships which are a harmonious part of engineering education.

Each year faculty and students grew in understanding of the aims of the Carnegie Plan and what it might achieve. Some students, to be sure, were unhappy that Tech's "Skibos"—long known to intercollegiate football fame—failed to live up to their game-winning reputation. To protests from students, Doherty's answer registered impatience with false emphases on college campuses, and with educational compromises which sometimes help winning football teams to be recruited. "Maybe some of you came to the wrong college," he told students who called upon him to protest.

All of his ideals were not pleasing to all students. Nevertheless, as engineering students began to find the pleasure and value of standing on their own feet mentally, increasing numbers also began to find new enjoyments in reading literature and history, in understanding human and social problems, and in music and art. Doherty was very sure that life for the engineer could be enriched by cultivation of habits which increased appreciation of the arts. He himself had not found nearly as much time for his painting as he wished, but students in the Arts Schools found their President's paintings in some of Pittsburgh's fine art exhibitions. One picture—a self-portrait—won a first prize. Obviously this engineer-President of Tech could paint better than many of his Arts School students! They might run into him at one of these exhibitions, or at one of the city's churches or auditoriums—with his wife, his daughter, or his sons—where he had learned he might hear words coming from a mind which knew how to think a problem through.

Doherty lived as a whole man and a responsible thinker. He attempted to find better ways to develop students in their capacities to live as whole and eventually mature citizens. And he was a good citizen himself. Seeing that Pittsburgh had many faults and was not progressing as it should, he helped to organize a group of industrial and business leaders to try to make it a better city. As the first chairman of this group he worked with these men for years to clear the air of smoke, improve housing, develop parks, and plan in many other ways to make Pittsburgh more healthful and more beautiful.

The development of the whole man, for himself and for his students, was his aim. Toward it he worked with his tremendous fire and energy, aided by a wife who found ways to give her best to him and to his work, and at his retirement age he had lost no whit of his enthusiasm for education and his personal need for continuing to learn. Actually, he was glad to retire at sixty-five. A man like Doherty always has confidence in humanity, so he knew others could and would carry on the work he was leaving. As for himself, he was eager again for the next step. He intended to think through some problems about painting. How far could his techniques for thinking be applied in the field of art?

"I want to find out how to make exactly the color I want," he said. It was three months after his retirement and only three days before his sudden death. "You have a color in mind," he said, pointing to a spot on a blank sheet of paper on his desk where he was obviously "seeing" the color. "There must be a way—a teachable way—to analyze it, to see the principle beneath any color, and to achieve it with the precision with which an engineer or scientist measures accuracy. That's what I want to find out now—how to make precisely any color I want—and I'm going to have a lot of fun at it."

He had come firmly to believe that *if a person knows what he wants to do, and then relates every act and effort of his life to that purpose, success is bound to come.* "If only I can help you fully to understand that," he told his artist daughter, "I will have fulfilled my function as a father."

He had wanted to be an engineer, and then to help young engineers become better engineers, and then to help better engineers become better human beings. He had uncovered and developed capacities in himself all along the way. There was still something he wanted to do and, though it lay in the realm of art, not science, it was a development of the dominant desire within him to learn how to meet new problems and think them through on the basis of discoverable eternal principles.

So he built his new home in Florida with a studio in one

half of the garage and a window just as he wanted it. He was ready and eager for the next step when his physical life suddenly ceased. Already a generation of engineers and teachers who had lived within the sphere of his direct influence were carrying his ideal in their lives and adding to it their own creative contributions. For that was Robert Doherty's effect upon people. In the highest sense of the word he was an educator. His inner fire kindled the creative instincts of his fellow men.

Ralph Edward Flanders

(1880 –   )

MECHANICAL ENGINEER, WHOSE EXPERI-
ENCE IN DESIGNING MACHINES HAS SERVED
HIM WELL IN THE UNITED STATES SENATE

□□□□□□□□□□□□□□□□□□□□□□□□□□

Is engineering experience a
valuable asset for political life? Probably most Americans
would answer "Yes" to this question. They believe men
and women of high character, trained and experienced in
a wide variety of useful work, are needed in politics, and
that engineering is a useful work.

With the exception of Herbert Hoover, twentieth century engineers have rarely become national political figures.
Ralph Flanders is an exception. He went to Washington in
1946 and again in 1952 as U. S. Senator from Vermont—a
self-educated mechanical engineer, a man of high moral
character and purpose whose life had been spent in the
development of machine tools and the machine-tool industry. His had certainly been a useful work, for machine
tools were essential for mass production, and mass production had put into the hands of millions luxuries that had

once been available only to the wealthy. His first few years in Washington convinced him that engineering experience has value for a man in the Senate. It develops "tough-mindedness" in thinking, and this, he says, is needed by men in legislative branches of government as well as in its administrative work.

Tough-mindedness as Senator Flanders thinks of it does not mean getting tough with the other fellow. It has to do with the inner attitude and quality of thinking a man brings to any problem he faces. It means complete discarding of wishful thinking for sound realistic thinking based upon fundamental principles and all known and discoverable facts. Though there may be exceptions, *an engineer's work compels him to face results exactly as they are.* According to Senator Flanders, this is a good habit to bring to lawmaking, and to the task of formulating policies which are to be the basis of our relationships with other countries.

Illustrating what he means in terms of his own engineering specialty, "You can't fool yourself long in designing and building a machine," Flanders says. "If a machine doesn't work, you can't pretend it does. On the basis of his knowledge of the principles upon which it has been constructed, the engineer looks for the 'bugs' that keep his machine from working and irons them out if he can. If it still does not produce the results it was built to produce, the engineer must accept this as a fact. He cannot say wishfully, 'Maybe if we give it time things will come out all right' as law makers sometimes assume. A machine designer has to accept facts head-on, and if they are not what he wants he has to go on from there to solve his problems with the increased knowledge failure or partial success has given him."

Successful government "for, by and of the people," says Senator Flanders, "must be based upon sound human principles quite as thoroughly as machinery must be based upon sound mechanical principles." This does not mean people are machines. No one has insisted more emphatically than Senator Flanders that men are mental and moral beings with the priceless heritage of a spiritual nature. Nevertheless, men living in the same world with each other have created "social machinery" to help regulate their relationships with each other. And tough-mindedness in facing facts about our social machinery is needed.

Senator Flanders' progress to a position where few engineers have preceded him came about through a very natural step-by-step development. For this reason it has a soundness missing in the lives of those political figures who have made vote-getting their aim before they had any sound achievement or experience. It happened also, Flanders insists, without struggle, and the person who wants to understand his life must accept the sincerity of his conviction that his life has been without struggle.

It began in the small farming community of Barnet, Vermont, but within a few years the Flanders family moved to a small farm near Pawtucket, Rhode Island, where the wage-earning head of the home became foreman in a woodworking shop. Ralph started to school when he was eight and on his first day learned to spell cat and rat and also about *amo, amas, amat* which his teacher had taught some older girls in another part of the schoolroom. His healthy curiosity gave him an interest in learning what the older pupils were being taught. The result was that he was prepared for high school in four years.

"I could not have done that in a graded school," he says. And it had been no struggle for him to achieve what he did.

High school courses in those days were different from modern high school curricula. To complete the college preparatory course at the Central Falls, Rhode Island, High School which he entered at twelve, Ralph had to work off four years of Latin and three of Greek as well as history,

English, mathematics, science and other subjects. Fortunately his course also included contact with an excellent educator. Mr. William Overton, principal of the school, was a true scholar himself and a teacher who could interest a student in subjects as diverse as the classics and mathematics. Under Mr. Overton's creative stimulation, Ralph's intellectual curiosity was fed and trained so healthfully that the process of learning would be for him of lifelong duration—and this continuing capacity to learn, rather than academic degrees, is the mark of the truly educated adult.

Several months before his sixteenth birthday Ralph was graduated from high school. Colleges lay near at hand and he was eager for more education. But he knew that, as the oldest of nine children in a family needing financial help until more of them were of an age to help themselves, he would not be able to go to college. This was no decision he struggled to make. He accepted a share of family responsibility as normally as he would have accepted going to college if his family could have afforded it. He looked upon his need to work and earn not as a handicap to education but as a turn in the road by which he would acquire education from this time on.

Conscious that within him was the mechanical bent of his New England ancestors, Ralph now looked forward to developing his talents in the usual New England way. The Brown and Sharpe Manufacturing Company of Providence, Rhode Island, accepted him as an apprentice and his father posted the necessary one hundred dollars to be forfeited if his son failed to finish the apprenticeship to which he was indentured—or "bound out," as the term was—for three years. Actually he remained with Brown and Sharpe two years after his apprenticeship was completed, finishing off with a valuable year and a half in the drafting room. Since he had taken, during his apprenticeship, the International Correspondence School's course in mechanical engineering which gave him some stiff college mathematics, Flanders now had a mathematical, a draftsman's and a practical mechanic's foundation which rated well as preparation for mechanical engineering in that day.

Nor had he neglected the cultural aspects of education. A revolution in American book publishing in his youth had made the best books available in editions selling for as little as fifteen or twenty cents. On the meager pay and long hours of an apprentice Ralph squeezed out some quarters to buy the classics and some time to read them.

Now began a series of jobs with machine tool firms which, because they specialized in different types of machinery, could give a budding engineer new opportunities to learn as he earned. Nor was there struggle in finding the kind of jobs to make this possible. As an apprentice he had begun to contribute to the two important technical journals in his field—*Machinery* and the *American Machinist*—and New England firms were on the lookout for young men writing about machine improvements well enough to be published in these journals. Actually it was through one of his apprentice-day contributions that he met his future father-in-law. The famous machine-tool designer and builder James Hartness, long president of the Jones and Lamson Machine Company in Springfield, Vermont, and later governor of that state, picked up his *American Machinist* one day to find that a young apprentice down in Providence had published a description of an improvement in a machine operation. It happened to be an improvement which would interfere with a patent Hartness hoped to take out when he had brought to successful completion a new machine he was then working upon. He asked the young man to come up to Springfield to talk with him and when the interview was over, Mr. Hartness would have been glad to keep Flanders in Springfield at that time if the right opportunity had been available.

Instead, openings came elsewhere. Flanders had a year in a Woonsocket plant; then worked with two different concerns in Nashua, New Hampshire, where he learned about and designed machinery for making paper boxes. After that (because he wanted to learn what working in a big plant could teach him) he took a job at the Lynn works of the General Electric Company. He learned quickly that he did not like a big plant, and in 1905 became an associate editor of *Machinery*, a position offered as a result of his many contributions to that journal which had proved he not only understood but could write about machinery with complete clarity. Continued reading of the classics doubtless had its influence in this.

The editorial position offered opportunity to inspect industrial plants from the Atlantic to the Pacific, and to examine many types of machinery he could not see in New England. It also meant opportunity to live in New York City where he had access to the best technical library in the country. For five years he took full advantage of what the editorship of *Machinery* offered. On the cultural side he visited museums, the opera, churches, concert and lecture halls, and indulged himself in reading. He enjoyed walking trips in the country and up the Hudson with New York friends. On the job side, in addition to the regular duties of an editor of a technical journal, a series of articles which he prepared for *Machinery* became the nucleus of his first book, *Gear Cutting Machinery*, which illustrated and described every type of gear-cutting machinery of American or European design in use at that time. A highly technical paper on interchangeable gear-tooth systems, of particular interest to the newly developing automobile industry and published by The American Society of Mechanical Engineers before Flanders was a member of that Society, attracted more attention than did his book.

Of his work and his pleasure in this New York period,

Mr. Flanders says, "As usual, I did only what interested me. There was no set plan—no struggle to accomplish what had been planned. As I looked back over those years later I realized they had worked out as though they had been planned in detail. I suspect this was because I was following my genuine interests and in doing so prepared naturally for the next step. If a man is lucky enough to have interests, and follows them, I think this is likely to happen."

It was the paper on interchangeable gear-tooth systems that was primarily responsible for the offer that now came from Vermont. The Fellows Gear Shaper Company in Springfield, friendly neighbor to the Jones and Lamson plant where he had talked with Mr. Hartness, offered him a position as their sales engineer. Flanders accepted. In less than two years he had married Miss Helen Hartness, and in another few months had moved to the Jones and Lamson plant where her father was president.

Yet this was certainly to be no step into the boss's shoes by marrying the boss's daughter. Flanders was taken on because the Fay Lathe, which Mr. Hartness had purchased from another firm, was still in a stage where it promised more than it delivered. Jones and Lamson needed an A No. 1 engineer experienced in machine design to develop the lathe beyond the promising stage. Flanders was offered a position with them as manager of the Fay Lathe Department, with responsibility for making that lathe produce results. That he took out more than twenty patents in the years he was with Jones and Lamson speaks well of their choice. But a full twenty-one years would elapse before he would step into the boss's shoes, and when that step happened no one could doubt that Flanders had earned the shoes.

Those twenty-one years in which he solved many a hard problem in machine tool design and operation and some equally hard problems in industrial plant management were, Flanders insists, without personal struggle.

"Fate never closed down on me," he says. "The door ahead always opened when I needed it."

As he sees it, he merely continued, at the Jones and Lamson plant, to follow his genuine interests and accept the work it took to keep up with them. He had learned the art of patience from his mother and had developed his capacity to enjoy each day's work. As the years passed, his achievements made him a nationally recognized authority in the designing and building of machines, especially on the engineering problems of screw threads and thread grinding. And because Ralph Flanders' interests had never been confined to the technological aspects of engineering, it was only natural that he began to be recognized as a man of vision in the field of industrial management, too. The human problems of the people with whom he worked had always interested him. As he assumed management responsibilities, it was only natural that he would do something about these interests, too.

Flanders' conscious interest in the problems of other human beings had begun in early youth. As a schoolboy he had once lived along a street leading to the gate of one of the largest textile mills in the world and he had been impressed by the appearance of the workers who entered the mill long before daylight of a winter morning to emerge long after dark. He had never been able to forget the sight of child workers, or of stunted, narrow-chested, sickly men and women who were the inevitable product of child labor and undernourishment, or to forget the sound of the club-footed and other crippled workers who made their trek past his window morning and evening.

Nor had he forgotten something about human beings he had learned when he was an apprentice. The employees of Brown and Sharpe, working a six-day, sixty-hour week year in and year out, had circulated a petition which he had signed, asking for a half holiday on summer Saturdays. It was a reasonable request, yet no employee had had the courage to risk the Company's displeasure by being the one to present it. The teen-aged Flanders had that kind of courage and had presented the petition. He believed in human justice and he believed in human beings—whether in the shape of employers or of fellow employees. He knew then, and later experience confirmed it, that good and bad in human nature were to be found in both groups. In fact, they were to be found side by side in each individual.

So, in following his diverse natural interests in his first twenty-one years at Jones and Lamson, Flanders found his education taking a new and important step forward. He had been faced with labor shortages during World War I and, a few years later, by the unpleasant sight of men who wanted to work and were unable to find work. He had learned that a man's job depended not only upon local conditions but upon the healthfulness of the whole economic system of which local industry was one small part. To a man like Flanders this was a challenge toward sound education in economics. He wanted to understand the principles beneath the economic machine as thoroughly as he knew the principles beneath the machines he helped to build in the plant.

Flanders knew well the road to education. He met the new challenge head-on, and by the early 1920's, when he served a year as president of the National Machine Tool Builders' Association, he was being listened to with respect when he spoke at meetings of engineers and industrialists on economic subjects. He spoke with pride of the fact that in America a higher standard of living was enjoyed by a greater proportion of our population than had been attained anywhere else in the world. He asserted with conviction that this high standard was basic to the American way of life, and that our economic system could and must find ways of continuing to secure the greatest good for the greatest number.

By this time Flanders recognized clearly that mass unemployment in the twentieth century was a threat to the American way of life. Such unemployment was very different in effect from unemployment in an earlier day when so great a majority of our people raised part of their own food and needed time for it. He said bluntly that new types of social responsibility were a necessity in a nation which had been so quickly transformed from a rural into an industrial nation. The more he studied our economic system as it existed in a Machine Age, the more he was convinced that mass unemployment was unnecessary in a nation with America's brain power and natural resources.

By the time the full force of the greatest depression of all had struck, the man who would later go to Washington as U.S. Senator was emerging above the old head and shoulder lines of the engineer and plant management man. He had stepped into a position of leadership in industrial and economic problems long before he stepped up to the presidency of Jones and Lamson in 1933. He was an engineer plus—an engineer with a social message. He was writing on economics for some of our most erudite journals. He lectured at universities. Some of his ideas were published in a very readable book, *Taming Our Machines*, in 1931. That his views won respect from fellow engineers was proved by his election as president of The American Society of Mechanical Engineers for 1934.

Still another facet of his character was apparent in what he was doing and saying. His economic ideas were always based upon a conviction that no economic system could be sound for America which did not rest upon acceptance of the spiritual nature of man as endowing him with certain rights, and that men of all other nations were likewise endowed by God with inalienable rights. Flanders was and is a man of deep spiritual faith. As a child he had learned in his home about God and prayer in a child's way. As he had grown to see the world about him with a man's eyes he had grown to see religion, too, with a man's eyes. The home he and Mrs. Flanders were creating was not merely one of human love, of good books and good music. It was a home where faith in God and habits of prayer were passed quietly along to children. Religion was not something to be worn on one's sleeve, and faith was not something to be acquired and clung to through denial of intelligence. Religion and faith were woven inextricably into the whole of life, to grow along with a man's intellectual capacities and help him reach his full powers as a human being. Flanders could speak about religion or he could be quiet about it. But he could not live without it, or divorce from its spiritual foundation his tough-minded thinking on any problem which touched human lives as economic problems did.

And so by following his genuine interests and not shirking the work they brought to him, Ralph Flanders came to the place where public service became a natural next step. He wanted to help preserve and develop the sound aspects beneath the American way of life, and to do it from as influential a position as possible. He decided, therefore, to try for the Republican nomination for the United States Senate, though success in this would mean giving up his salary from industry, and all business connections. He was not a rich man by current American standards and in 1940 a senator's salary was still insufficient for a senator's needs. Flanders had achieved enough leeway in his financial status, however, to make it possible for him to sever his ties in the business world and still carry his obligations as a senator and a family man.

Up to this moment he had never sought a job without

indications that the job was his if he wanted it. So not only was he an amateur in politics in 1940; he was a total amateur in job-seeking, too. He failed to get the nomination. The door to the Senate did not open to the first knock.

In some ways it may have been just as well. With America facing stupendous tasks as the arsenal of democracy for World War II, competent men in industry were greatly needed. Flanders kept his shoulder to the wheel of the machine tool industry and on national advisory boards where his services were sought. The Big Depression had long since disappeared. Prosperity—or what was called prosperity—had returned to New England as elsewhere in America because of another war. Was there any fundamental soundness in this kind of cure for unemployment? Flanders thought not.

A few years after his defeat for the Senate nomination another door leading to public service opened. He was appointed president of the Federal Reserve Bank of Boston. Not only could he do an engineering and executive job here in installing better management practices in the Bank's procedures, he would have opportunity to help "unfreeze" certain funds so that they might serve small industrial plants fundamental to the New England way of life. Flanders thought this way of life—workers living in small industrial communities where they had homes and gardens, or on small farms on the outskirts of such communities—was sound and productive of human satisfactions. He believed a small percentage of the billions of dollars invested by life insurance companies, savings banks and other such organizations in gilt-edged securities only might properly be released to support the kind of free enterprise which produced this way of life. Cooperation with business men, and with the faculties of the Harvard Business School and Massachusetts Institute of Technology resulted in the formation of the American Research and Development Corporation by means of which hitherto frozen funds became socially productive in the way Flanders had visualized.

Two years later he ran for the Senate again and now this door opened, too. By the time Flanders was accustomed to his chair in the Senate the world was in a mounting state of tension. America, and soon Russia, had the atom bomb and if another war were allowed to happen, destruction threatened not only the American way of life but innocent people everywhere. Yet war threatened, and economic problems were part of the threat.

America's problems were intensified because fear and hatred had been roused against us among peoples who had once been friendly toward us. As is always the case, our admitted sins could be made to weigh most heavily against us, so racial discriminations that had long been practiced in America became an effective weapon for those who wanted to rouse other nations against us. But lies as well as truth were used against America, and if freedom were to continue to exist and to grow on earth, America needed the friendship of all who loved freedom. All of this Senator Flanders knew, and he knew also that the Senate could exert strong influence in our relations with other nations to help them recognize truth from falsehood.

In characteristic manner he went about his new job, facing the facts as they were, not as he would have liked them to be. He reached his decision on the basis of these facts. Whatever else his senatorial duties were to be, his primary aim would be to make our foreign policy one that would enable freedom-loving people everywhere to recognize the truth about freedom-loving people in America. He would support measures to make America strong physically, of course—so strong any nation on earth would hesitate to attack us. But the strength of the spiritual unity possible between freedom-loving peoples is the greatest strength of all, and our foreign policy should more definitely cultivate that strength.

Within a comparatively short time Senator Flanders was delivering a series of short speeches on the Senate floor urging definite steps in our foreign policy to cultivate this unity. To explain briefly all he urged and has been urging ever since is not possible. But it is rooted, as may be expected, in his belief that the moral law, and not old ideas of diplomacy, is the only sound basis for our relationships with the people of other nations, because transgression of the moral law, like transgression of a physical law, carries its own punishment.

"If a man decides to walk on air, and steps out a window," he told the Senate one day, "the results of the transgression of physical law are inevitable. The same is the case with the moral law." If senators wanted to ask "What is the moral law?" Flanders added they could find it in the Old Testament, which is a history of man's search for the laws of the universe, particularly in the One Hundred and Nineteenth Psalm. Then let them turn to the New Testament and read Jesus' words about loving God, and "thy neighbor as thyself."

It is fortunate for America that patience is one of the Flanders' virtues for the thing he wants to do requires patience. If he can come to the end of his service in the U. S. Senate and still be able to say that his life has been without struggle, it can be attributed to the quality of his patience. He says that in his youth his mother used to quote the Thirty-seventh Psalm, "Rest in the Lord, and wait patiently for him." Later he heard the familiar words speak anew to him through the music of Mendelsohn's *Elijah.* The words still have meaning to him—to wait patiently and fret not because of the man "who bringeth wicked devices to pass"—and they help make of him a man greatly needed in public life today. The engineering profession has bestowed the Hoover Medal "for distinguished service" upon Ralph Flanders, and it may well be proud of him. This engineer with eight years of formal education carries an honorary doctorate from Harvard, honorary Phi Beta Kappa from Dartmouth, and honorary membership in Tau Beta Pi from the Massachusetts Institute of Technology. Exactly how this engineer's name is to be written upon history's pages as a senator, is still unknown. But if those pages ever record a rating of senators who, as men, developed human greatness and understanding within them, Ralph Flanders will stand high on the list.

Arthur Ernest Morgan

(1878 —   )

CIVIL ENGINEER, SPECIALIST IN FLOOD-
CONTROL WORK, FORMER CHAIRMAN OF
TVA, ORIGINATOR OF ANTIOCH'S WORK
AND STUDY PROGRAM, BELIEVER IN THE
SMALL COMMUNITY AS THE FOUNDATION OF
DEMOCRATIC LIFE

◼◻◼◻◼◻◼◻◼◻◼◻◼◻◼◻◼◻◼◻◼◻◼◻◼◻◼◻◼

LIFE looked uncertain that autumn day in 1900 to the tall, lanky young man of twenty-two who had just returned to St. Cloud, Minnesota. Three years earlier he had started out in search of health and an education. With health far from rugged and only a brief six weeks of college work back of him, he was home again —home to the community where his parents had urged him, earlier, to curb his ambition for college and settle down to a life of light work.

Handicapped as Arthur Morgan still was from the effects of cerebral meningitis in early childhood, his parents may not have been unjustified in urging him to accept light work. After several years in which his recovery had seemed doubtful, they had watched him grow into a thin, nervous little fellow, so frail that his mother had been thankful, when their house was enlarged, that her son no longer had to climb the outdoor ladder leading to the attic where he slept. Temperatures in St. Cloud sometimes reached forty degrees below zero, and the cracks in the Morgan attic were wide enough to let the snow drift through.

Then, when Arthur was ten, measles affected his eyes in a way which made reading difficult and interfered with his study. Added to this, he grew so rapidly that at fifteen he measured six feet against the kitchen door jamb and weighed only one hundred and thirty-five pounds. No wonder his diary for those days speaks of physical discomfort which made him wish, at times, that his early illness had been fatal.

Yet uncertain health did not keep Arthur from a boy's normal recreations. He was a nature lover with a taste for adventure which sometimes led him into danger. St. Cloud was located on the Mississippi, and one of his ways to spend a Saturday afternoon was to seat himself on a log and steer himself through rapids and quiet waters to some spot from which he would walk home, searching for botanical or geological specimens on the way. When the river was filled with logs, things might get out of hand in running rapids and avoiding submerged rocks. There were times of uncertainty—as once when a floating log struck a rock, swung violently to hit his own log, and gave him what he later described as a "brief period of concentrated interest." But often the most interesting part of the trip came on the way home when he found some new species of lichen to add to his already extensive collection.

Nor did uncertain health keep young Morgan from working. Arthur's father, a surveyor, knew almost whole plays of Shakespeare by heart, solved mathematical problems for the fun of it, read scientific journals and had his own improvised chemistry laboratory in the woodshed. But he pursued surveying spasmodically, and Arthur's ex-schoolteacher mother took in boarders to help out. As a sixth grade schoolboy her son began to raise and sell vegetables. Later he worked on near-by farms. For a few months of his last school year he walked four miles to a farm each midday, worked there, slept in the hay and walked four miles back to school each morning.

Attending school off and on as health permitted, Arthur got altogether between two and three years of high school and succeeded in graduating. He had long since developed the habit of thinking for himself, and because he had definite ideas about what he had wanted to get out of school, he saw how his own schooling had failed to meet some of his needs. He recognized, for example, a lack of intellectual curiosity in the way his high-school courses had been taught. To Morgan, the world was teeming with interest and seething with questions, but little or none of this had come to life in classes. His desire to explore the reasons why people believed as they did, and acted as they did, met no stimulation and little response from teachers. His interest in botany and other sciences roused questions in him about the causes of the diversities of individuals of a species of plant or animal. His interest in the human race made him wonder why brothers and sisters differ as they do. Nothing in his high-school work or in his contact with his teachers had adequately fostered or faintly satisfied his innate intellectual curiosity, and he had begun to dream of and plan a school of his own where all the normal needs of young people—including health and financial needs—would be met.

"Be careful," someone has said, "what dreams you have in your youth, for they may come true as the years pass."

As he left his high school in St. Cloud, one of the lacks he felt most keenly was help in choosing a calling. Faced with small chance of going to college, he felt he needed help here and the high school provided nothing in this line. His health handicap imposed limitations, too. He thought of surveying, but his father urged strongly against it. "In a pioneer country, surveying is a dog's life," was the elder Morgan's opinion which the son was to understand better when he, too, ate the impossible food, spent evenings in the highly malodorous log cabins, and slept in the vermin-infested beds of immigrant farmers. So Arthur took the jobs that were immediately available. He taught a country school, worked in harvest fields, loaded rock in a granite quarry.

At nineteen he decided to leave home for a period and be on his own. Because of ill health, he had been sheltered. He wanted to prove to himself that he could stand alone, so he started out one September morning with a dollar and a half, and a bundle containing a small Testament, a copy of Gray's *Elegy*, his diary, a cyclopedia of universal information, writing materials, and other minor items. By appointment he met a friend and started on his way. They found work at husking corn. After two weeks the friend returned home. Alone, Arthur walked to the Mississippi, tied two logs together with a clothesline, sat on them cross-legged with his bundle beside him and started down the river. He was bound for Minneapolis on his way to Colorado for health, independence, and an education.

In Minneapolis he started overland for the West. It was October 1. Autumn was in the air and a thousand miles or more lay between him and Colorado. He found jobs along the way, milking cows or husking corn. By October 22 he was in Iowa where he slept that raw night in a haystack. Then he found work on a farm, husked corn until his fingers were bleeding. A kick in the chest by a horse nearly proved fatal. (It troubled him for years.) By late November he had reached his cousin's home in Denver.

That autumn of 1897 was a period of severe depression. Once in Denver he answered an advertisement for a chambermaid to work for her board and was told he was the seventeenth *man* to apply. Then he went into the mountains and cut timber at an elevation of 8,500 feet. Six months later, at Boulder, when he registered for some courses preparatory to university work, he had a job of a sort and remaining capital of $1.45. In a few weeks his eyes gave out. He rented a small fruit ranch adjoining the University campus. To keep going during the summer he bought vegetables from Texas, hauled them by horse and wagon to remote mining camps and sold them.

Whenever he could find a few hours he read biology, general scientific theory, literature, poetry and philosophy in the University library. The next fall he was able to register as a University freshman. In six weeks his eyes brought his college education to a final end. He decided that his spare time while at work would permit as much study as his eyes would stand.

He now thought he saw a way to be socially useful while making a living. Having noticed the lack of books in farmers' and miners' homes, he bought a wagonload of cheap edition literature—Emerson, Ruskin, Carlyle, Thoreau, Kipling, etc.—and started to sell it in homes along the edge of the mountains. He soon found that his prospective customers did not have the vocabulary, reading experience or interests to make useful reading of these books possible. But he and the fifteen-year-old boy who made the trip with him slept in midwinter under the stars, shared the horse's meal when food gave out and read some of the books. Then, to replenish the money bag, Morgan took a job digging coal in a mine near Trinidad, was nearly caught in a mine cave-in, then badly shocked and nearly electrocuted by a poorly insulated live wire.

All these and many other experiences were back of

Arthur Morgan that autumn day as he approached St. Cloud where conditions at home had made his return seem imperative. He found work, first cutting cordwood in the forest, then as timekeeper in a quarry. To some it may have looked as though his life up to now had been but a blind and aimless stumbling, but it was far from that to the young man who was living it. Despite the fumbling which was a natural result of his limited education and experience, he had been trying to achieve some definite results. He had been searching for a calling which would help him build a healthy body, would allow growth and self-education, and permit him to maintain his somewhat unconventionally exacting ethical standards.

A year after his return to St. Cloud Arthur made a decision. Surveying would provide the outdoor life his health required and provide the income he needed as he continued his self-education. He persuaded his father to let him work as a laborer on a surveying job. Soon he was accepted as an assistant. After six months of practical experience and the limited study his eyes permitted, he bought a second-hand surveyor's outfit, went to work for himself, and soon found surveying merging into engineering.

In 1902 he interrupted his growing private practice in St. Cloud for about eight months to take part in a survey of the pine lands of the Chippewa Indian Reservation along the north boundary of Minnesota. The job paid eight dollars a day—a gold mine to Morgan. His health was still far from rugged and the weather that winter was frequently thirty below or colder. When the four men working as a party got beyond the limits of Indian pony and sled haul, they carried their camps on their backs. At night they put their sleeping bags on a bed of spruce boughs on a spot of ground scraped bare of snow. They spent the entire winter in the north woods with only a thin tent for shelter at night. Their food was mainly "sourdough" bread they baked for themselves in a reflecting oven, and occasionally moose meat. As spring came Morgan had to wade day after day in the great swamp north of Red Lake, Minnesota, where a foot of water covered the winter ice. The physical hardships he put himself through (hardships he later called unnecessary risks "taken because I did not have enough confidence in and respect for my life's prospects") left him in better physical condition than when he started out.

He resumed his private practice in St. Cloud and found increasing engineering opportunity in the reclamation of wet lands which were widespread in the state. His work came to the attention of the governor and he was offered an appointment as State Engineer for Minnesota, a job concerned chiefly with land reclamation. He declined, however, because he doubted his competence for the job. Another reason was that he had recently married a young physician who had come to St. Cloud and did not want to be away from home most of the time, as acceptance of the job would have necessitated. Within a year his wife had died of typhoid, and at twenty-seven Morgan returned to his parents' home with a motherless son to be cared for.

By this time Morgan had a toehold in engineering, but in such fields as bridge design or sanitary engineering he was hopelessly outclassed by men with university training. Land reclamation had been an entering wedge, but if he were to become a competent engineer he must more thoroughly master some branch of the profession. At that time no one was well-qualified in flood control and reclamation of wet lands, so Morgan knew he could have a nearly equal chance in that field providing his underlying science was sound. So he sought drainage jobs and, since Minnesota's drainage laws were very inadequate, made a thorough study of drainage laws in other states. He then prepared a new code for his own state and got it approved by Minnesota's

Engineers' Society. With that approval, the State Legislature quickly enacted it as a law.

In working out that code Morgan had made the acquaintance and sought the counsel of nearly every interested person in Minnesota. Two years later he had one of the largest drainage engineering practices in the State, with a dozen engineers on his payroll. His work quickly attracted the attention of the directing head of similar work in the U.S. Department of Agriculture who asked him to take Civil Service examinations to make him eligible for supervisory jobs in Federal drainage and flood control work.

With his Civil Service appointment as a supervising engineer, Morgan left his Minnesota practice with a younger engineer. His new work would enable him to associate with well-trained engineers on larger and more varied projects. It would enable him to discover what part of the country would be the most promising locality for that kind of work. It also enabled him, on coming east to Washington headquarters, to consult an unusually able eye specialist. The new glasses, he noted in his diary, "will mean a great deal even at this late date if I can begin to read and study seriously. I am not well prepared for my work." He was thirty years old when he wrote those words.

From this point on, Arthur Morgan's progress seems almost phenomenal. His first job in his new appointment was in the San Luis Valley of Colorado where excessive irrigation was bringing "alkali" to the surface and ruining the soil. The problem called for intensive study and was solved for the particular conditions dealt with. His next assignment was in Louisiana. Several other assignments followed. Then he was put in charge of the second largest such project ever participated in by the Department of Agriculture—the reclamation of the St. Francis Valley in Arkansas. These Civil Service jobs brought Morgan face to face, in some instances, with superiors whose orders sometimes seemed to Morgan to be in flagrant disregard of government funds. With his exacting ethical standards he chose to disregard orders at times and stay on the job until his work could be really useful and government investments socially productive.

At the end of two years (in which his new glasses had served him well) his engineering education and experience had advanced to the place where he was able to resign from government service and, with a partner, Leroy Hidinger, establish their own engineering firm in Memphis, Tennessee. At twenty-six he had not felt competent to be State Engineer for Minnesota. At thirty-two he had confidence that the Morgan Engineering Company had ability to plan and execute land reclamation and flood-control projects of any size the country should present.

Jobs came quickly. While in government service Morgan had directed some large exploratory projects financed jointly by federal government and several large lumber companies and planters who had a program for cutting timber from Mississippi River bottom lands in Missouri, Arkansas, Mississippi and Louisiana, and then of reclaiming and selling the land for agricultural purposes. Land owners now called on the new firm to direct the large reclamation projects in process of development. These assignments led to others, and in a comparatively few years Arthur Morgan had become an engineer of national repute, perhaps the foremost figure in the United States in the reclamation of wet lands and flood control. His water and drainage codes had been adopted in half a dozen states and his engineering projects had involved the outlay of millions of dollars in a dozen or more states. Two million acres, or more, of fertile lands had been reclaimed for man's use in Tennessee, Arkansas, Missouri, Minnesota, Louisiana and Ohio. Thousands of miles of drainage canals had been built, mammoth dams, bridges and levees constructed. All had been done with the help of competent specialists, to be sure, but under the judgment and direction of Morgan and his partner.

After the disastrous Dayton, Ohio, flood of 1913, costing several hundred lives and doing two hundred million dollars' worth of damage, Morgan was appointed chief engineer of the Miami (Ohio) Conservancy District charged with designing methods of water control which would prevent recurrence of such a disaster. This thirty-million-dollar flood-control project became the first large-scale undertaking in America to use dams for the control of floodwaters. Instead of letting contracts, he bought equipment, organized working forces and did the work directly. His employment of engineers grew from the dozen he had employed in St. Cloud to more than two thousand during his years of engineering practice.

The Dayton project was successful and a truly mammoth work for its day. The carefully written reports of engineering research which Morgan initiated on that project are still international authority in their field. Nor was his direction of the project limited to the physical aspects of an engineering job. Arthur Morgan became an agent in a democratic venture, a pioneer in dealing with the human and social issues of a job like this one. Good labor conditions were as important as good concrete. When a dam was to be built, therefore, a complete village was set up, not the tarpaper makeshift so often constructed elsewhere. Disreputable construction-camp surroundings were eliminated. Each village had its waterworks, sewers, and electric lights, its schools and comfortable homes for workmen's families, as well as a comfortable bunkhouse and mess hall for men without families. Food in the mess hall was good. Ex-President Taft's former chef was head of his commissary department. Morgan himself spent countless hours on personnel problems. Labor discontents were part of the American picture of the day and he cooperated with labor leaders in formulating fair and reasonable labor policies and codes in what had been a non-union field. This course resulted in efficient, economical labor as well as in the successful working of democratic principles.

In this type of engineering-plus achievement he found human satisfaction. Yet Arthur Morgan had never lost the dream of his youth of establishing a school which would meet the normal needs of young people in such ways that the full unfolding of their human capacities would be encouraged. This interest was stimulated by his marriage, in 1911, to Miss Lucy Griscom, a young biologist-chemist who was a member of the Wellesley College faculty. In 1915 they came to the conclusion that the time had come for them to get into the educational field where they could put some of their ideas into practice. They went so far as to purchase a site for a school in Massachusetts. For the time being, however, Morgan's responsibilities as president of the Dayton Morgan Engineering Company, and in handling the Miami Valley project prevented their entering actively upon their educational venture.

Then, toward the end of this vast flood-control project, an event happened which changed the plans the Morgans had been making for a school of their own. Arthur Morgan was appointed, without his knowledge, to be a trustee of a small college in Yellow Springs, a few miles from Dayton. He submitted a plan for reviving it, making it a pioneer educational venture. The outcome was his appointment, in 1920, to the presidency of Antioch College, charged with putting his proposed program into effect. While not so unconventional as the program he had had in mind for his own school, the program was in some ways new to American education, and was based upon his conviction that education should be concerned with developing the whole of the student's personality.

The part of the Antioch program which most high

school and college students know about was the arrangement whereby a student alternated five (or ten) weeks of college classes with a similar period on a full-time job. This was a step toward taking care of students' financial needs which Morgan had been aware of in his own high-school days. Another feature was the organization of the college into a democratically run community of faculty members and students in which all alike would explore the best ways of living together in community life. By such means Dr. Morgan hoped Antioch's young people could be graduated in five or six years not just *from* college but *into* responsible positions or associations where, as men and women of liberal and practical education, they would become instigators of intelligent and effective democratic living.

In a very few years the college in Yellow Springs had become a vital education experiment. The student body doubled and doubled again. Ex-President Eliot of Harvard spoke publicly of Antioch as the most interesting educational project then being attempted. A Dayton engineer, Charles F. Kettering, established on its campus the Kettering Foundation for the study of photosynthesis, to study how green plants use sunlight to produce plant tissue. A Philadelphia friend who shared Dr. Morgan's long-time interest in the development of human personality established the Samuel S. Fels Research Institute for the Study of Prenatal and Postnatal Environment. In time Antioch was no longer an experiment, though it retained the experimental attitude. It had achieved an established place in the academic world. Furthermore, in faraway India, an educational revolution partly inspired by Antioch and promoted by Gandhi, was under way.

As he was developing the Antioch program Dr. Morgan, like his students, alternated academic and practical work. He continued to direct large projects of the Dayton Morgan Engineering Company and to serve as its president. With Antioch's success he was now an outstanding figure both as an engineer and an educator in fields other than engineering. And this engineer-educator was the man President Roosevelt chose, in 1933, to become chairman and one of the three directors of the TVA—the Tennessee Valley Authority project. "I have been reading your 'Antioch Notes,'" the President told him, "and I like your vision."

Taking with him the core of his engineering staff, trained on other jobs, Morgan had a great dam under actual construction within ninety days after Congress had brought TVA into being. To achieve these rapid results, as in the Dayton flood-control work he did not let contracts, but assembled a staff, bought equipment, and did the work directly. As administrative head of this project and as chief engineer in charge of dam and powerhouse construction, Morgan had several hundred million dollars worth of construction under his personal direction in the next four years. An over-all plan for the control of the Tennessee River was developed, a series of dams along the Tennessee and its tributaries was planned, and several of them, including Norris, Wheeler, and Pickwick were completed during his years of service, while others were well along in construction. Design and engineering efficiencies had their full consideration, and these dams made records of economical and quick construction. However, as at Dayton the human and social aspects of the construction work were given a degree of attention almost unprecedented.

In the midst of the TVA work (1936) Dr. Morgan resigned from the presidency of Antioch College. About this time differences of outlook had arisen among the TVA directors as to the accuracy of statements and presentation of policy of the TVA power program—a program which called for the sale of electric power in a tax-supported project. Dr. Morgan criticized majority policies and in 1938 was out of TVA.

He was now sixty years old and free to undertake whatever work seemed most necessary and productive. He would continue his engineering activities as president of the Dayton Morgan Engineering Company, but on a part-time basis as when he had been at Antioch. His experiences as an educator had clearly shown him the deep influence of the early childhood years in the development of personality. Not home and school environment alone, but the community in which home and school existed was of great importance in determining how men and women would use their powers throughout life. He had gradually come to the conclusion that the small community had played a part in human affairs far greater than was generally realized. The decay of small community life, he had come to believe, was one of the principal causes of the downfall of great civilizations, and would have the same outcome in America unless the people should become aware of the fact and take effective action.

In this belief he formed, in 1940, a non-profit organization, Community Service, Inc., to which he might devote the remainder of his life. Its object is to provide professional assistance and counsel for revitalizing small communities, through its statements of social philosophy, its conferences, lecture and consultation services, its loan library, correspondence courses and publications. In a dozen years the work had carried beyond the United States to India, Finland and Canada.

One of Dr. Morgan's useful contributions to the Service has been his book, *The Small Community*, which is a general treatment of the subject. Another is his book, *A Business of My Own*, written because he knew how much of the decay of small community life had been the result of lack of economic opportunity for young people in their home communities. This book lists, with actual examples, hundreds of small businesses which can be undertaken in a small community. His *Industries for Small Communities* was still another attempt to help build an economic life in America that would stimulate the growth and health of communities small enough to offer the advantages he believes are inherent in this type of environment, for young and old alike.

It is Dr. Morgan's belief that man is by nature a "small-community animal," and that the change from having 85 per cent of America's population living on farms in 1790 to only thirteen per cent living on farms in 1950, with tremendous population growth in large cities, has been accompanied by a disintegration of community life which is far from healthful in its promise for the future.

Primarily this engineer-educator-citizen is trying to foster the values which make a nation great and develop capacity for fellowship. Fellowship, quite as much as leadership, is needed for the days now upon the world. His engineering work has rehabilitated millions of acres of land in America. He would like to see more intelligence in the societies men create for themselves. Engineering, plus education, plus good citizenship have made up his lifework and to Dr. Morgan's friends they have been somewhat like the Biblical virtues of faith, hope and love. The greatest of these is love, and his good citizenship has been an unsentimental expression of Arthur Morgan's love for his fellow men in whom he has faith, and for whom he has great hope, provided they are given the right environment in youth.

Vannevar Bush

(1890 –   )

ELECTRICAL ENGINEER, INVENTOR OF A
"MECHANICAL BRAIN," WHO AS WARTIME
DIRECTOR OF OUR NATIONAL SCIENTIFIC
RESEARCH CONTRIBUTED TO AMERICA'S
EARLY SUCCESS IN THE USE OF ATOMIC
ENERGY

⬚⬚⬚⬚⬚⬚⬚⬚⬚⬚⬚⬚⬚⬚⬚⬚⬚⬚⬚⬚⬚⬚⬚⬚⬚⬚⬚

WHEN for the first time in
American history a Government Agency was created to
mobilize scientific effort on a national scale, an engineer,
Vannevar Bush, was appointed to head it. Immediately
some of our most highly respected scientists spoke up to
assert their confidence in the fitness of this particular engineer for so important a position in the scientific world. In
his successful handling of his post as Director of the Office
of Scientific Research and Development during the six
years of its existence, an engineer brought new honors to
the profession of engineering as he won the personal respect
of scientist, engineer, military leader and informed layman
alike.

Vannevar (pronounced Va NĒ′ var) Bush had taken a

very definite path to the unique position he was to hold during and after World War II. Yet, as a boy, illness had seriously delayed his start. Born in Everett, Massachusetts, on March 11, 1890, the son of a Universalist minister, he was interrupted in his early school work by periods of sickness which deferred his graduation from the high school in Chelsea, where the family had moved, until after he was nineteen. Minor illnesses, mainly rheumatic in form, finally culminated in a major attack of rheumatic fever which necessitated a year out of school in one continuous period. He accepted the precautions essential for complete recovery and then, with the rheumatic fever finally licked, began to make up for lost time.

Entering Tufts College in the fall of 1909 he finished the five years of work required for the bachelor's and master's degrees in the next four academic years. During those years he had lost one whole semester because of a ruptured appendix, but he earned a considerable part of the expenses entailed during the other seven semesters. A few years later he completed in one year, at two of the stiffest higher educational institutions in the country, the two years of work required for a doctorate in engineering. He had native brilliance, but he was a worker, too.

As a boy Bush knew that he wanted to be an engineer. He was one of the country's first schoolboy radio fans, which fact had something to do with making choice of a lifework easy for him. During his high school days, on what must have been one of the earliest homemade sets built by an American schoolboy, he picked up radio-telephone conversations when that art was still in an experimental stage. This happened not only before most high school boys were building radio sets but, since Marconi's first message from England to Newfoundland was not sent until 1901, it was before most people had any personal experience with radio at all. It helps explain why the teen-aged Bush knew so definitely when he was ready for college that he wanted to become an electrical engineer.

At Tufts, faculty and students alike recognized him as unusually able in mathematics and that was to help him in more ways than one. He did not need to use hours of his time plugging at his math courses as do some young men who chose engineering as their profession and he turned his unusual gift to cash value through tutoring freshmen in engineering who found mathematics a serious stumbling block. Cash was not without importance to the son of a minister in a family where two older sisters had already been helped through college, and Tufts students needing and able to pay for help were plentiful. Eventually Bush (always an executive) was able to organize his fellow students in evening classes where a half dozen or more could be taught with a very little more time than it took for the individual tutoring of one—with cash receipts considerably better than for one.

His ability to help students open their minds so that they could grasp mathematics did not pass unnoticed by the faculty. In his third year in college he was made an assistant in the mathematics laboratory where he instructed freshmen. When one of the professors became ill Bush, while still a student, was permitted to teach regular college classes in first-year mathematics.

In 1913, with his B.S. and M.S. in electrical engineering, "Van" Bush headed straight for the test engineer's course at General Electric as Bob Doherty had headed for it two years earlier. His beginning salary was $11.20 per week, but the variety of experience offered by this one-year course was more than a by-product for a young man of Bush's aspirations. Rather, it was the other way around. "I wanted to be an engineer," he says of himself at this period. And to Bush that meant more than a master's degree and a well-paying job where he could practice what he already knew. It meant he was looking forward to further academic work necessary for a doctorate, and wanted a well-chosen variety of practical experience to buttress and sharpen him for the advanced academic work.

The test engineer's course gave him invaluable experience as did a period in the Inspection Department of the U.S. Navy. But money was essential, too, and an academic year teaching mathematics at his Alma Mater enabled him to finance the one year in which he hoped to complete the two years of work required for his Ph.D. It happened that the coming academic year was during the brief period when work for a doctorate in engineering at the Massachusetts Institute of Technology, toward which Bush was aiming, could include appropriate graduate work at Harvard, with the doctorate granted by both institutions. This practice was soon discontinued and Dr. Bush is one of the few men alive today who hold this degree. He received it in the spring of 1916.

To anyone interested in "what makes an engineer tick" Dr. Bush and Dr. Doherty offer striking similarities and contrasts. While still young men in their twenties, each was beginning to achieve recognition as an extremely promising young engineer. While still young in his professional life, each made brilliant contributions to electrical engineering which brought acclaim from their peers and eventually earned for each the Lamme Medal of the American Institute of Electrical Engineers—one of the highest honors that can come to an electrical engineer. Likewise, each exhibited marked administrative gifts all along the way—Doherty in industry and Bush in the educational world. But something motivating each man was in marked contrast with the other.

Doherty, on the one hand, in a position in industry which promised high advancement in the administration of scientific and technological research, was urged so irresistibly toward teaching and the broader problems of engineering education that work in no other than the educational field could satisfy him. Bush, on the other hand, in a high administrative position in the educational world and aware of many satisfactions, found himself challenged so much more greatly by the administrative angles of scientific and technological research that he was ready to leave the academic field when greater opportunity offered elsewhere.

Moreover, strange though it may seem to many who have never possessed the gifts or achievements of these men, each was willing to relegate to a secondary position in his personal life the type of research that had brought him personal recognition and high honors. Surely the lives of these two men show clearly that even though gifts and talents may dominate the original choice of a profession, something in the man himself must finally determine the full direction his life is to take.

Vannevar Bush's first move after he had earned his Ph.D. was to return to Tufts (with Phoebe Davis as his bride), as an assistant professor—not of mathematics this time, but of electrical engineering, and with some time free for consultant work. Obviously firms were not looking for consultants whose experience did not qualify them as specialists in some field, but Bush, though only twenty-six years old, already had such qualifications to offer. As radio research and development had leaped ahead, he had kept well in the forefront of some of it. One of his early clients, the American Radio and Research Corporation, whose laboratories were situated a few miles from Tufts College, now asked him to serve as their consultant. This made a good set-up in every way but it was interrupted by American entry into World War I and Bush's services on submarine detection for the U.S. Navy. With the war's end he went back to the educational world, this time to M.I.T. as associate, then full professor of electrical power transmission, in charge of graduate work and research. Directing this latter work at an institution like M.I.T. had great possibilities for a man of Bush's originality. Moreover, faculty members at M.I.T. had considerable opportunity for consultant work. Throughout the thirteen years Dr. Bush was a teaching member of the Institute's faculty, he was serving as engineering consultant in the industrial world as well as bringing things to pass in the Graduate School's laboratories which had never happened anywhere before. Certainly his teaching was never of the ivory tower variety charged against some engineering college professors in those days.

He found time, too, to write textbooks that were greatly needed in a technological field in which twentieth century science had necessitated so many changes. There was a book *Operational Circuit Analysis*, dealing with a field in which he was one of the pioneers, and before that, a text with W. H. Timbie, *Principles of Electrical Engineering*, published first in 1922 but with new editions keeping it up to date into the 1950's. Teaching and its ramifications offered scope and held appeal. Nevertheless, when opportunity presented itself in 1932 to become vice president of M.I.T. and Dean of Engineering, he accepted. Administrative work was his aim and now he gave up not only his teaching but all consultant work as well to enter upon administrative work on a full-time basis. It was at approximately the same time that Dr. Doherty left a high administrative position in industry to enter the educational field at Yale. Bush retained, as Doherty did too, his interest in some of his researches.

It was in the years of his professorship at M.I.T. that Bush began to win recognition for pioneer contributions in electrical engineering fields. His inventive genius had begun early to focus upon mechanical means for reducing the burden of computations and calculations upon the human mind in work where repetitive routine processes are necessary. Soon the math shark at Tufts became the designer and builder of machines which could release men's minds from much effort of this kind. One of the earliest of these mind-labor-saving devices was the network analyzer for reproducing and studying accurately in miniature the operating characteristics, under stresses of various kinds, of any big power network.

But the device with which more laymen are familiar—by name, at least—is Bush's "mechanical brain" or, as engineers and scientists speak of it, his differential analyzer, which may be described as an "intricate calculating machine capable of solving complex ordinary differential equations." His first machine of this nature (various models of it were soon built in other parts of the world) was built at M.I.T. in 1930 in collaboration with the electrical engineering staff. The new version—an electronic version—construction of which began under Bush's direction in 1935, was completed in time for it to work day and night throughout World War II on problems vital to our defense—problems in atomic physics, acoustics, ballistics, electrical machine transients, and various other fields. This machine, weighing one hundred tons, combines some 2,000 electronic tubes, several thousand relays, about one hundred and fifty motors and nearly two hundred miles of wire. It is capable of providing solutions of differential equations expressing mathematical problems involving as many as eighteen variables.

The importance of these so-called mechanical brains is greater than many laymen realize because they do not understand the extent of the mathematical calculations which are a time-consuming, work-delaying part of modern scientific and technological work. Nor do they recognize that a truly brilliant worker in this field may not have the mathematical faculty for making calculations essential to his work and must—whether he prefers it or not—depend upon others who have this faculty.

Dr. Bush made important contributions, too, to the development of thermionic tubes—those radio tubes which, as he has described them, control great forces under the guidance of less power than a mosquito uses to vibrate its wings —tubes which, although consisting of spider webs of metal sealed in thin glass containers, can be tossed about in packages, picked up, plugged into a socket, and become illuminated with a brilliant glow. Under the guidance of skilled engineers and technologists these tubes are manufactured by the hundred million today and sold for a few dimes each, yet they demand such precise location and adjustment of gossamer parts that a master craftsman, using the most skilled hands in the world, would have to work months to build a single one of them.

Surely it was fascinating and rewarding research on which Dr. Bush was engaged at M.I.T. where, despite a heavy administrative job demanding long hours of work each day, he still found time to direct his favorite researches. From his administrative chair he was finding satisfaction, too, in surveying the whole engineering curriculum and attempting to make it a more effective instrument in aiding teachers to prepare students to perform what he considered to be the central function of the engineer—to apply science soundly. He wanted work in the engineering school to enable young men to develop and use two contrasting mental attitudes—the analytical and the practical. The analytical attitude, as he has described it, "involves the willingness to take pains in order to be sure. It disowns superficiality and guesswork . . . Its keynotes are thoroughness and vigor." Yet—and this is often surprising to young engineers—genuine proficiency in the practical attitude is (according to Bush) harder to acquire than proficiency in the analytical attitude. Rigorous thinking is essential as a buttress against the wishful thinking a young engineer is often tempted to indulge in when he meets a hard new engineering problem. Bush wanted the engineering school at M.I.T. to train young men in rigorous thinking, and he won respect for many of his educational ideals as well as confidence in his administrative ability from the group he worked with, from President Karl T. Compton through all ranks of the faculty.

Meanwhile war clouds were hovering again over Europe. Hitler and the results of German technology were becoming more and more a threat to freedom. Vannevar Bush knew, as well as any man could know, the meaning of science to modern warfare and the need for preparedness against any modern dictator aiming at world power. So, when the Presidency of the Carnegie Institution of Washington was offered to him, he knew how much more it offered, in such a year as 1938, than merely the administration of the funds of an organization created to "encourage investigation, research and discovery, and the application of knowledge to the improvement of mankind." It meant a position in our national capital toward which national leaders turned naturally for consultation on problems involving science and technology. It meant a position of great influence in preparing America for what was threatening in Europe.

It was a trained investigator with well-proved executive experience who went to Washington to assume, on January 1, 1939, responsibility for administering one of the largest non-governmental research budgets (about a million and a half dollars annually) in existence. It was an administrative job requiring wisdom of both the human and scientific variety. The Carnegie Institution fostered individual and group researches in fields as far apart as interstellar space, terrestrial magnetism, geophysics, archaeology, plant biology, genetics, and embryology. Bush carried the burden of it effectively. In return, the work gave an engineer new insights into the whole field of science, a vision which could increase his comprehension of the possibilities of the engineering job of applying science soundly.

Within a few months after his arrival in Washington, World War II and the Blitzkrieg broke with a speed and fury unknown to man before. Hitler's war weapons not only rained hell upon armies and non-combatants alike in Europe but struck fear into the hearts of many Americans in influential positions. Pressure was brought to bear upon President Roosevelt to ask England to surrender at once to prevent the horrible carnage of war's new weapons. Dr. Bush was one of those who did not scare in this direction. With the cooperation of President Conant of Harvard, President Compton of his own M.I.T., Dr. Jewett of the Bell Telephone Laboratories and others, Bush suggested to President Roosevelt that a National Defense Research Committee be formed for the purpose of supplementing the work of the Army and Navy in creating weapons to win the war which Hitler had precipitated upon the world.

Democracy, by its very nature, moves slowly. Yet in this time of crisis it moved with intelligence and without too much delay. Before many months had passed Vannevar Bush walked out of President Roosevelt's office with "O.K.FDR." initialed on the memorandum Bush had prepared, outlining proposals for the formation of the National Defense Research Committee. Shortly afterward—in June 1940—he received the letter from the President formally authorizing him to go ahead with the plans, and containing the specification that another committee, recently appointed for study of the possible relationship to national defense of recent developments in the fission of uranium, would report directly to the new committee of which Bush was chairman. "The function of your Committee includes this special matter," the President wrote. And thus it happened that Vannevar Bush would head the organization responsible for the application of atomic science in the creation of the atomic bomb.

A year later this "NDRC," as it was called, became a part of the newly established Office of Scientific Research and Development (known as OSRD) of which Dr. Bush was made Director, and which included, too, the newly formed Committee on Medical Research. This was 1941, and by December of that year—approximately Pearl Harbor Day —atomic research had progressed to a place where, because of what it now promised if prosecuted with the best intelligence of all scientific groups necessarily concerned in it, the decision was made for an all-out effort in this direction. As a member of the Top Policy Group headed by the President, and as Director of the OSRD, Bush shared responsibility in this decision and for determining further policies even after administration and development of the atomic program had been taken over by the Army.

What happened as a result of all this is history whose immediate results no American needs to be told. But what is not so generally known is that, for the first time in history, scientists and engineers had been recognized as more than consultants to fighting men. They had become full and responsible partners in the conduct of war. The ability and personality of the engineer who directed the scientific efforts of thirty thousand men and women working as teams of scientists and engineers on new weapons and new medicines and collaborating with the military as they did so, had a great deal to do with winning the war and saving scores of thousands of wounded men from death. It is tradition in America that civilian and military do not work together easily. To the civilian, "top brass" had long been a term denoting military arrogance no civilian accepted easily. During World War II part, at least, of this tradition was dissipated. America had been breeding military men like Marshall and Eisenhower as well as scientists like Bush and Compton and Conant. Under the influence of leadership like this, scientist and engineer civilians at top levels argued it out with admirals and generals and in most cases they ended up as friends. The democratic process worked in a realm where it had never worked before, and a civilian engineer, challenged by the possibilities of the administrative angles of his chosen life work, had reached the place where, in national emergency, he made history.

So widely has Dr. Bush's part in all this been recognized by leaders in the educational world, that he holds honorary degrees from a score of these institutions. A dozen medals and awards from scientific and technological groups have been pressed upon him. England made him Knight Commander of the Most Excellent Order of the British Empire. At the White House he received the Medal for Merit with bronze oak leaf cluster. And the end, doubtless, is not yet.

Through the war years, the facilities of the Carnegie Institution and the skills of its staff of scientific investigators were made entirely available to the Government for war work. Many important research and development projects were carried on. After the close of the war, Dr. Bush, who had continued as President of the Institution throughout the period, led in restoring the normal programs of basic research on a broader foundation. As early as the fall of 1944 President Roosevelt had asked him to recommend ways whereby the lessons learned during the war might be applied in time of peace "for the improvement of the national health, the creation of new enterprises bringing new jobs, and the betterment of the national standard of living." Bush's answer, published in 1945 under the title of *Science, the Endless Frontier,* drawing upon studies made by scientists, engineers, and educators in attempting to answer this question, is available in almost any library today as is his later book *Modern Arms and Free Men.*

But no matter how much he might prefer to put most of

his efforts into peacetime scientific fields, the peace of the latter 1940's and of the 1950's became an uneasy peace. So to a man in Vannevar Bush's responsible position, a man of deep belief in the democratic way of life as a good life for children to grow up in, the problems of adequate defense seem likely to occupy a great deal of his time as long as threat to American freedom remains. Not that he is a man to be driven by fear. He is a man to lead in the intelligent overcoming of fear. He believes that free men are potentially stronger than are men who submit to dictatorships, and that freedom is worth fighting for when, or if, fighting becomes the best immediately possible way to gain or retain freedom.

Dr. Bush believes that modern science and technology offer great possibilities for winning peace on earth. He knows war was born in men's hearts long before modern science was born. He believes science will force men to do away with wars. To that end he worked until his retirement, in December 1953, as President of the Carnegie Institution, and has continued to work since then through the many channels open to him as an individual deeply concerned in the still pressing problems of peace and war.

Scott Turner

(1880 —   )

WORLD-TRAVELED MINING ENGINEER, EX-
DIRECTOR OF THE UNITED STATES BUREAU
OF MINES, WHO DIRECTED THE FIRST COM-
MERCIAL COAL MINING WITHIN THE ARCTIC
CIRCLE

■■■■■■■■■■■■■■■■■■■■■■■■■■■■■■

FIFTY years ago mining en-
gineering offered as much opportunity to see the world as
joining the Navy offers a young man today. Three years
after Scott Turner had received his Engineer of Mines
(E.M.) degree, he had mined in practically every state in
the West and had prospected, sampled and assayed ores at
Veraguas Peak in Panama, with a necessary stopover in the
yellow fever- and malaria-ridden Canal Zone for his supplies. In the next five years he included Alaska and the
Yukon in his itinerary, and after that North Africa, Spain
and England. So it is not surprising that, in his twenty-one
years of mining engineering practice before his appointment as Director of the U.S. Bureau of Mines, Scott Turner
had had mining experience in twenty-one countries.

"Maybe if I had to start again, facing conditions as they

are now," he says, "I might be influenced by all this talk about security, and not move about and take the risks we used to enjoy. Perhaps it is better to start at the bottom with some big company and devote your life to getting advancement within that one organization. Such things are a matter of choice—if a young man can get the chance to choose. Then, too, opportunity to pioneer in new mines and new places is considerably less today than in 1900."

Turner got the chances, so he had choices to make all along the way. They led him into a migratory and adventuresome life, and he has never regretted it. "Make up your mind never to regret your choice," is advice he has passed along to other young engineers. "Study facts, analyze information, get advice. But the final decision on any next step is yours alone. Take it—and go ahead. Don't look back or take time to be sorry."

Yet—and this is important—Scott Turner took no chances about building a solid educational foundation before he started out on his travels. He grew to manhood in a period when young men were able to attain success in mining without any college education at all. More than four years of college work was far from usual, probably even a rarity in the profession. Despite Turner's love of action and the out-of-doors, he accepted the discipline of six years of college work before he let his venturesome spirit help decide what he was going to do next. After the long hewing to his purpose had been accomplished, he was able to choose his adventures to add to his education. He liked new experiences, new jobs, new places. But new jobs were undertaken for the planned purpose of making him a more competent mining engineer, and this has been an important factor in his personal success.

Michigan, where he was born July 31, 1880, was a mining state in its pioneer stages during Scott's youth. At seven, his father took him inside a mine for the first time.

On the walls of the Turner home in Lansing were cabinets filled with minerals to which Scott's father occasionally added new specimens. His remarks, as they examined the minerals, often included, "Now when you study mineralogy, son . . ." or "When you take up the study of metallurgy, you will discover that . . ." So Scott never put much thought upon what he was going to do when he was grown. He moved naturally along toward mining engineering. His environment, both in his home and outside it, clearly indicated this direction.

At eight, he had another experience which left its imprint for life. He was presented with his first man-size shotgun. Partridge, duck and rabbit were plentiful around Lansing. (They were good food on the family table, too.) Summers in Michigan's Northern Peninsula brought new hunting and fishing experiences. Scott killed his first deer when he was thirteen. Bigger game came later and hunting and fishing remained a lifetime recreation. He was edging up toward sixty when he brought down the huge black bear which won for him first prize in the National Big Game Hunter's Competition for 1938 as the best kill of the year. Fishing tales are of similar magnitude and veracity, but they belong elsewhere!

It seems a little surprising, in a young man of Scott Turner's active interests in the out-of-doors, that he did not want to shorten the indoor preparation for the profession that would set him out on his adventures around the world. Instead, by the time he had graduated from the Lansing High School, he had decided to take some work in the liberal arts before he specialized in mining engineering. He thought then, as he still thinks, that a cultural background as a foundation for a technical education is a decided asset. So, although his major study at the University of Michigan was geology, he registered for an A.B. degree. He worked off as much mathematics and science as the curriculum leading to a bachelorate in arts permitted. This would enable him to take more of the more highly specialized courses later in the Michigan College of Mines. But he took the time necessary to base his later technical schooling upon the foundation of a liberal arts education which broadened his cultural outlook and taught him the value of clarity in the use of the English language.

This latter, Mr. Turner has always felt, is one of the great needs in a mining engineer's education. Many a business company, which has made a heavy financial investment in getting a new mining venture to the point where an engineer's opinion and detailed report are essential for next decisions, has found to its dismay that the mining engineer does not know how to present information in a clear-cut manner. Turner's employers never had that problem to meet. And his fellow engineers have had reason to be grateful for the clarity of his many technical papers (more than fifty) which have helped advance their profession—a type of contribution for which Mr. Turner feels young mining engineers should hold themselves responsible.

His college work in geology was good enough to make his professor want to take him, the summer following his graduation from the University, as his field assistant on a U.S. Geological Survey party in Idaho and Oregon. For sixty dollars a month Turner helped Professor I. C. Russell with geologic and hydrographic work, did much of the cooking for their party of four, and often took care of the horses. Then came two years of specialized work at what was then the Michigan College of Mines in Houghton, and in the spring of 1904, with a B.S. and an E.M. added to his earlier A.B., Scott Turner was ready to continue his education on jobs instead of in the classroom. His immediate ambition was to fit himself to become superintendent of any type of mining operation and run it successfully. Since, to his way of thinking, a man in such a position ought to know how to turn his hand to any job done by the men whose work he would superintend, Turner knew he still had a lot to learn. "But I figured I was now ready to get paid for learning the mining business from the ground up," he says, "instead of having to pay for the privilege of learning."

In those days, employers or their representatives were very seldom in close contact with engineering schools, as is more usual today. Young mining engineering graduates usually rustled their own jobs, spending payless days or weeks calling on mining men and visiting offices in mining camps or cities. Turner landed his first job at Tombstone, Arizona. He started work as a miner, but was promoted quickly to surveying, sampling and geologizing; he built and operated a small concentrating and cyaniding mill. He was getting along well, but the horizon soon seemed too narrow, so he moved along to other mining districts.

As to surveying and assaying: "I did not want to waste valuable time looking through an 8-inch pipe at a plumb-bob string, or cooking samples in a laboratory," he says, "so I joined with another engineer who felt as I did about learning the practical fundamentals of the business, and became a tramp miner and millman."

His early technique was to apply for a miner's or mill-man's job, stay on it as long as he felt he was learning something new, then move on to another mine where, for the same day's wages, he could learn something he did not yet know. Since his bosses were often glad to discuss geology and their own engineering problems with him, Turner learned a great deal about mine valuation and operation through his experiences at many camps where varied types and grades of ores were being mined and beneficiated. During this period, he performed many types of mine or mill work, while working for day's wages.

The examination of ores in Panama came early in his

career and was followed by mine examinations in Nevada. Before and after these jobs, came work as miner or millman in gold camps of Nevada and Colorado, in lead-zinc mines at Leadville and in northern Idaho, and experience in mine-sampling in various states.

Then Turner was fortunate enough to become associated with T. A. Rickard on the editorial staff of the Mining and Scientific Press in San Francisco. Here he spent eight happy and profitable months, enlarged his acquaintance among local and itinerant mining engineers, and improved his writing through the tutelage of a great technical editor.

Becoming restless again, he left California to become superintendent of a mine in Nevada. Next he joined the engineering staff of F. W. Bradley, one of the leading engineers and operators of that period, and spent some time at the Tacoma smelter. Bradley then loaned him to T. A. Rickard, whom he accompanied on an inspection trip to the Yukon and Alaska, where he learned more about dredging and placering alluvial gravels. Their job took them to many places, including Dawson, Hot Springs, Fairbanks, and Nome. Rickard then sailed for home, leaving Turner at Nome to do a special engineering job for the Wild Goose Mining and Trading Company before he rejoined Bradley's staff.

Out of a clear sky, he soon received an offer to become mining geologist for one of the largest American mining companies, with headquarters in Boston. He spent two years in the West at this work, studying geological problems, directing diamond-drilling campaigns, and examining and sampling mines, principally copper and gold.

All of this experience was basic to Scott Turner's successful handling of an unusual job he decided to accept one day in London, in 1911. Earlier that year he had been sent to make examination of certain mining properties in North Africa. Arriving at Tangiers he had found warships of several nations lying in the harbor and the international situation so tangled he could not get permission from the French commandant to travel through Fez to the properties he had been sent to examine. After investigating iron ore deposits near the Morocco Coast he went to Spain and from there to England where he spent some time in the tin mines in Cornwall. It happened that, when he got to London, T. A. Rickard was there, too. Through him and other engineering friends Turner began to meet some prominent people in the mining world. The result was that one Friday he found himself with three good offers in his pocket, the final choice to be made the following Monday.

One offer was to become manager of a copper property in Argentina. The second was to examine gold and other metal deposits in eastern Russia—with his tickets over the trans-Siberian Railway to Vladivostok already purchased. The third was to accompany an American, Mr. John M. Longyear, on an inspection trip to examine and give an opinion on iron-ore deposits in northern Scandinavia and on coal deposits in Spitsbergen, the development of which the partners, Frederick Ayer and Mr. Longyear, were then considering.

"It was a tough decision to make," says Turner. Each job would take him to a distant country. He was now thirty-one, and this decision would influence the future course of the professional life into which he had poured so many years of sound preparation. Each opportunity offered something attractive and something different—gold mining, copper mining, coal or iron.

"Right or wrong, I chose coal and iron," he says, and proceeded at once with Mr. Longyear to northern Norway, where Turner examined the iron-ore deposits on which his employers had options. Then he and Longyear went to Spitsbergen, where Turner made a thorough examination of the coal property on which Longyear's company had already started small-scale operations. Turner gave his opinion on the engineering and economic aspects of operating here on a commercial scale, and returned to America to resume practice of his profession here.

Before the year was out Mr. Longyear, who had been seeking a competent mining engineer and executive with the personal qualifications to fit him for the hazardous job on the Spitsbergen archipelago on which several men had already failed, persuaded Turner to become Ayer and Longyear's European manager and undertake commercial operation of coal mines on the Island of West Spitsbergen.

The new job became the first long-term job in Turner's career. And what a job! The whole archipelago was uninhabited except for men employed by Ayer and Longyear. Spitsbergen was a "No Man's Land" over which no nation claimed sovereignty. Following accepted international practice, Ayer and Longyear set up claim-posts, hoisted the American flag, and established sovereignty over 600 square miles, underlain by all the important coal beds. (These claims were duly filed with the State Department at Washington, where, subsequently, annual progress-reports were deposited.) No court had jurisdiction over crimes committed there. The only laws were those written by Turner into contracts made with imported employees.

No mining had ever been done this far north on a commercial scale before. Turner himself had mined for a period in Nome, Alaska, but Nome was now one thousand miles southward. Longyear City, the name of the new camp, was nearly 900 miles north of Iceland's north tip, and only 720 miles south of the North Pole—"too far north even for the Eskimos." Boats could get in and out of its harbor during four months of the year at most. The first ship attempting it might be locked in an ice pack for weeks or, if it did arrive, might not be able to get nearer than twenty miles from shore. In that case, men and supplies had to be moved twenty miles over the ice. The last boat left in September—possibly October—and the men who saw the boat depart had to settle down for the long winter night, knowing there was no access to the mainland for eight months. There were electric lights and a small wireless station, but radio in 1911 had not reached the entertainment stage.

Turner's job was, briefly, to organize the office work, hire workers from an office in Tromsö, Norway, and transport them to the island, design new buildings and equipment, complete the building of the electric power station, extend the railways, build docks and ropeways, concrete bunkhouses and other buildings, purchase supplies and machinery, gather technical men from the United States and mine bosses and foremen from England, find customers for the coal, charter boats for conveying it and see to it that the coal was delivered. Among the first necessities, of course, were topographical maps to indicate the contours and coal seams on the island, and then prospecting parties to locate the coal. These parties soon found coal outcrops at fifty-two widely scattered points.

Mine entries were established at these points, slopes driven into the coal, and commercial operation got under way. Nobody knew exactly which way, or ways, of mining would be best for the Spitsbergen coal. In order to test comparative costs, Turner divided an area of the best seam into separate panels. Some panels were mined under English supervision by English methods and others under American supervision by American methods. Nor did anyone know the best ways of using Spitsbergen coal. Tests were made of it in actual practice so Turner could give suggestions to his customers. The coal was actually of excellent quality for a number of purposes. Norway's merchant marine was soon using it, and some of the Russian wood-fuel locomotives on the Murmansk Railway changed to coal-burning grates and used the coal successfully.

During the five years in which he successfully operated the mines, Mr. Turner chalked up some achievements worth noting. First of all, though danger of explosion in this type of mining was great, he guarded effectively against that danger. One precaution was in the use of explosives. Spitsbergen-coal samples were sent to the U.S. Bureau of Mines for tests, and formulas for a safe explosive for coal blasting and for rock work were determined. (In truth, his men were better guarded against explosions than many men in coal mines in the United States in that period.) Safety lamps were used, a large ventilating fan installed, and proper precautions insisted upon about times at which explosives could be used. True, the fact that all the men used Copenhagen snuff instead of cigarettes or pipes eliminated the danger of matches underground. But that the dangers were very real was proved when the principal mine was completely destroyed by a coal-dust explosion shortly after Turner had sold the mines to Norwegians and left Spitsbergen. Turner's achievements in safety are all the greater in view of the fact that the great bulk of his miners and workmen were Norwegians who had no experience in mining coal, were afraid of coal mines, and were learning new work under foreign bosses.

Another achievement lay in the good health conditions of his men—a factor which, like his low accident rate, made men more willing to undergo the isolation of working on Spitsbergen where there was no family life at all in the first years, no church, no school, no movie, no recreation hall. Turner's experience had taught him that more trouble could originate in a mining camp's boarding house than in its mines, and he guarded against that kind of trouble. Food of the best quality was purchased. It was well cooked and cleanly served. Arctic weather conditions made it easy to keep fresh meat and fish during the long winter night. He had been warned that scurvy would break out among his men. Expeditions to the Polar regions were always plagued by scurvy, and the vitamin-knowledge which now makes prevention of scurvy simple was not available then. Turner determined to supply his men not only with high quality food, but with a variety of it, including all that the Norwegians were accustomed to on the mainland. The Americans and British were given stewed fruits and other staples usual in their homelands, too. In five years, no scurvy appeared and no epidemic of any kind broke out. When the first boat would appear in the spring, the common cold would be brought in and would sweep the island. Then it would disappear, and without serious results.

The output of coal on Spitsbergen was increasing steadily when World War I brought new difficulties. Coal had to be delivered over submarine-infested waters. Ships, for time or trip charter, became scarce. The supply of men—Turner had up to 600 men at work—was seriously diminished because of war duties and restrictions. Explosives became difficult to obtain. At Turner's advice, his employers decided to sell the property and the Czar of Russia acquired an option. Back in the United States when the decisions about the sale were completed, Turner was sent to St. Petersburg (now Petrograd) to close the deal. He boarded the *Lusitania*, was injured when it was torpedoed, and spent five hours in the waters off the Irish Coast before he was rescued. After a month's hospitalization in London, he sailed from Newcastle for Bergen just in time for his ship to be under bombing from seven Zepplins before it got out to sea.

In Christiania he learned that water transportation to Russia had been discontinued. It took many interrupted days by train before he reached St. Petersburg. When he got there the Czar had fled, and no one had authority to make final payments. Turner returned to Norway, conferred with the King and the Prime Minister, attended a cabinet meeting, appeared before the managers of the branches of the Bank of Norway, spoke to a meeting of leading ship owners and industrialists, and succeeded in persuading them all that Norway needed to own this important source of coal. He then worked out the conditions of sale, and, eight days after this deal was consummated, he sailed for Peru, to be gone two years.

The five Arctic years were adventurous ones in Turner's life, but they did not end his travels. He signed up with a British-Belgian banking house, and spent the two years preceding America's entry into the war inspecting and reporting on mining properties in Peru, Bolivia and Chile. This South American job was the hardest and most hazardous he ever did. With but few assistants, he visited and reported on more than one hundred mining properties. At times he made long journeys by mule-transport to extremely inaccessible places, over rough trails, back and forth across the Andes, crossing swollen tropical streams by improvised rafts, and often living in tents for weeks at an altitude of about 16,000 feet. One of these trips required three months, much of the time on muleback. He saw practically all of the operating mines in these three countries, and sent back to England his conclusions and recommendations regarding properties inspected. He encountered many difficulties and dangers; incidentally, an emergency-operation was needed, and a Mexican doctor removed his appendix in Chile, at an altitude of about 11,000 feet. This kept him off muleback for nearly a month. He sailed from Callao for San Francisco shortly after the United States joined in the war, and was called to Washington immediately on arrival, given a commission as lieutenant in the Naval Reserve Force, and was on active duty until the end of the war.

The day he doffed his uniform, he responded to a call from Canada, and was appointed consulting engineer and technical head of The Mining Corporation of Canada, Ltd., which was controlled by the financial interests for which he had worked in South America. He spent seven active, interesting, and profitable years with this important company, which operated silver and other mines in Ontario, had mining interests in various other provinces, and conducted explorations and developments in the United States, Russia, China, Mexico, and Central and South America.

He examined, recommended, and took over for his company a huge complex-ore deposit in northern Manitoba, the famous Flin Flon mine, now known as the Hudson Bay Mining and Smelting Co. property. When he first saw it, it was, as he described it, "only a piece of moose-pasture, lying more than 100 miles from the nearest road or rail point," accessible only by long canoe journey. More than one hundred million dollars in dividends were paid from the operation of this mine in the next twenty-five years and in 1952 it was still going strong. Quite a mine, when you remember how recently it had been a stretch of wild marshy ground outlined by wooden location stakes!

And now came a change. One of Turner's friends in the mining engineering world, Herbert Hoover, was serving as President Coolidge's Secretary of Commerce, and he asked Mr. Turner to become Director of the U.S. Bureau of Mines. To accept would mean heavy financial sacrifice. It would also mean opportunity to do interesting and useful work in his own country under the leadership of a man he greatly admired. Mr. Turner's mining ventures had made it financially possible to accept the lower salary and continue to shoulder his personal responsibilities. On January 1, 1926, after having spent seventeen years in foreign countries, Scott Turner returned to his native land and became Director of the U.S. Bureau of Mines.

The Bureau was only fifteen years old at that time. It had been created to determine what had caused a series of major explosions in Pennsylvania and West Virginia coal mines, and its first duty was to make mining a safer occupation. But it had other duties, too, which offered Turner opportunity to direct many types of work of importance to his profession and to continue his own education as he did it. He still had a passion to know more about mining. He had had actual experience in coal, copper, gold, silver, iron, lead and zinc mines, and in many types of work in these mines. "But at the Bureau," he says, "I had about one hundred technical specialists in everything known to mining engineering, and it was like going to college all over again."

Since more changes in mining engineering methods had occurred in the first quarter of the twentieth century than had occurred in possibly the preceding nineteen centuries, it is not hard to see why Turner could feel he still had much to learn. The unusual thing is that he had not reached a state of mind in which he was ready to sit back and float along on what he already knew.

He remained at his post in the Bureau for nearly nine years. Under his direction were eleven Bureau of Mines' Experiment Stations in which expert engineers and scientists worked on the many problems of the mining and mineral industries. Each station paid particular attention to problems affecting the section of the country in which it was located. A few of the high spots in the Bureau's activities while Turner directed it included: silicosis studies and the silicosis clinic at Picher, Oklahoma; the erection of a helium-processing plant near Amarillo, Texas, which made the United States the only nation producing safe, non-inflammable helium gas for the dirigibles then being developed; potash drilling in the Southwest; oil-shale experiments in Colorado; experiments to determine the best way to ventilate tunnels, and to determine the cause and prevention of caisson disease afflicting deep divers, and men working under pressure. There was valuable work, too, in developing processes for treating complex, or low-grade ores profitably so they might contribute more to our national wealth. One of the best contributions the Bureau could make was in lessening waste of our national resources through inferior methods of mining and processing.

Publication of the *Minerals Year Book* was instituted during Turner's regime at the Bureau, as were studies of mining methods and costs. But, first of all, the Bureau's duty was to create better health and safety conditions for the approximately one million men then working in our coal mines, metal mines, quarries, oil and gas fields. Mining had a higher personal accident rate than any other major industry in the United States, and the Bureau's duty was to discover, to create, and to urge better safety methods. Accident rates had been lessened in the earlier years of the Bureau's existence and they were lowered further in Turner's years there. In coal mines (which had the highest accident rates), the lowest rates in the whole period for which statistics had been kept were achieved during the last years of Turner's regime, falling to a fraction below three lives lost for every million tons of coal mined.

By this time about one-third of our coal was mined in rock-dusted mines, a safety measure the Bureau had proved helped prevent explosions, but the use of which it had no authority to enforce upon mine owners. Safer types of explosives had been developed, as had safer miners' lamps and electric equipment. The depression, too, had something to do with the low accident rates toward the end of his work at the Bureau. Employers had tried to retain their best workers during lay-offs in this period and accidents caused by worker carelessness—always a large factor in industrial accidents—were diminished. Also, the Bureau's mine-rescue work which Turner had expanded to include as many as 100,000 men trained in a year, had decreased the number of deaths when an accident occurred.

The period in which Mr. Turner had been at the Bureau was the first time in his professional life in which he had been in this country continuously for any length of time. He made use of it in services which busy men find time for. He served on the U.S. Assay Commission; as delegate to international congresses of engineers in Tokyo, Berlin and Liege; as a member of the Anaconda Smelter Smoke Commission and, of course, in various safety promotion groups. Conspicuous among his voluntary services was his administration of his office as president of the American Institute of Mining Engineers during which he visited every local section of that organization. Conspicuous, too, were papers on mining and allied subjects in the technical and, occasionally, the non-technical press. Public honors and recognition came to him, including several honorary doctorates.

The result of it all was that when he resigned from his post at the Bureau of Mines he had many non-income-producing interests—still including hunting and fishing—to which he now wanted to give more time. But a man like Scott Turner could not give up mining engineering. He soon found himself serving as consultant to foreign governments as well as to mining companies. In fact, he found himself one day serving as an officer and director of nine mining companies, and doing a little mining on his own account, too. He was acting as arbitrator in mining disputes, and as expert witness in litigation cases.

Gradually he has permitted himself to devote more time to personal interests, and one of them has been in the field of guidance for young people who want to become engineers. He is not completely convinced that the young engineering graduate today, who may step directly from college into technical work far more often than fifty years ago, does not miss something valuable. Working as miner and millman is an experience he thinks worth having. But regardless of what a young engineer's first job may be, Scott Turner rates hard work, personal integrity and loyalty to one's administrative superiors as of vital importance. Mining engineering, he thinks, offers little to the young man who aspires to easy success through an engineering degree and a magnetic personality. It is a man-size job for a man-size man who is willing to put in years of hard work along the way to success.

Certainly Turner himself has never been afraid of work. His seventy-seventh birthday found him completing two years of service as President of the American Institute of Consulting Engineers. They were years in which he considered his office not an honor to himself but an opportunity to serve his fellow engineers and their public. Then came a highly prized award to crown his life of enduring achievement—the Hoover Medal, awarded by engineers to a fellow engineer for distinguished public service.

Neither honors nor years have been allowed to interfere much with Turner's work habits. Week day mornings find him in his office early. When he leaves it in the late afternoon for an hour's trip home he often carries work with him—papers and reports he wants to read before an interview or committee meeting the next morning. His present interests reach far beyond the engineering field but in the latter years of his eighth decade engineering is still his primary field of service as it has been from the days when he began the practice of his profession.

J. Brownlee Davidson

(1880 – 1957)

WHO SAW NEED FOR GREATER APPLI-
CATION OF ENGINEERING METHODS TO
FARM PROBLEMS, AND PIONEERED IN CRE-
ATING THE PROFESSION OF AGRICULTURAL
ENGINEERING

🔲🔲🔲🔲🔲🔲🔲🔲🔲🔲🔲🔲🔲🔲🔲🔲🔲🔲🔲🔲🔲🔲🔲🔲🔲

AGRICULTURE, the world's oldest industry, was extremely slow to reap the benefits of engineering progress. The ancient world had roads and waterworks which exhibited advanced engineering thought and methods. Its agricultural practices remained crude and primitive. In the more modern world, too, agriculture was slow to adopt adequate engineering methods. Only in the second quarter of the twentieth century did the agricultural engineer win high professional recognition, and even yet his work is often misunderstood.

What is agricultural engineering? J. Brownlee Davidson described it as "Engineering related to and organized around the industry of agriculture, in many respects as mining engineering is organized around the industry of mining." It was Dr. Davidson who developed, at Iowa

State College of Agriculture and Mechanic Arts, the curriculum which led to the first degrees in agricultural engineering. Those first degrees were not granted until 1910. Yet by 1952 all state colleges were teaching courses in, and more than forty were granting degrees in agricultural engineering. The new group, contrary to popular thought, was not employed primarily on farms, as mining engineers are often employed at mines. They were being used in manufacturing industries catering to the production of farm equipment and farm structures; by federal and state governments on problems pertaining to agriculture; and by financial organizations as consultants on farm problems. They had high professional status. But Dr. Davidson and fellow pioneers had had difficulties in creating this new branch of the engineering profession and winning for it understanding and respect from other engineers.

As a child, Lee Davidson displayed inner bents or talents, which had opportunity for development in the rural environment in which he grew up. He was born in 1880 on a farm near the small rural community of Douglas, in southeastern Nebraska, about fifty miles from the junction of the Platte River with the Missouri. The Davidson farm lay within the fertile arc made by these rivers as they approach each other, on rich plains where white farmers had but recently begun to replace the Indians.

Nebraska had been a state for only thirteen years when Lee was born but already it was one of our heaviest producers of cereal grains. From the Davidson farm Lee and his five older brothers and sisters looked across mile after mile of rolling fertile land to which corn and wheat brought variety of color as season followed season. Since the vast flat expanses of our Middle West had offered such profitable use for mechanical equipment, and since American inventive ingenuity was so great, more progress had been made in farm machinery in the few decades before

Lee's birth than had been made in the preceding five thousand years. Although iron, and then steel, were in use for plows earlier, it was not until the middle 1870's that steel plows had replaced, in general use, the wooden plows that had been in use since at least 3000 b.c. Yet in Lee Davidson's boyhood, horse-drawn corn planters, harrows, cultivators and binders were frequently in use on Nebraska and other Middle Western farms.

Farm machines interested Lee always. The first harvester he remembered was a machine put out by the Marsh Brothers which incorporated into its design a platform on which one or two men could stand and bind the grain. As a small boy he watched grain fall from this machine, while men working on the platform tied it into bundles with bands of straw. Such a machine seemed a wonderful invention to a small boy in the 'eighties. A little later he saw a harvester which used Spaulding's device for bundling the grain and Appleby's twine binder for tying it. This machine cut grain, picked it up, bundled it, tied it with twine, and dropped it in windrows without any human labor at all. After a hot day in the corn fields Lee wished there might be a machine which would help harvest corn so easily. Eventually he began to think about designing such a machine himself.

The Davidson children went to school in a community which, with the arrival of the railroad, became the village of Douglas. They attended the little rural church their parents helped to establish, and worked on the farm as did other farm children. On their farm was a shop in which ordinary blacksmithing and repair work was done. Apparently the youngest of the children showed unusual aptitude for this latter type of work, for he was the member of the family urged to do shop work.

"Mother thought I was a 'whiz' as a mechanic," Davidson often recalled. "If I reset a wagon tire, or sharpened tillage tools, or did any of the repair jobs constantly needed on a farm in those days, Mother had a keen eye for the quality of the work. She encouraged me by praising my repair jobs whenever she could and the family seemed to think I had a special knack for such things."

One by one the young Davidsons completed the work offered by the Douglas schools and went over to Peru to the State Normal College. When it came Lee's turn, the school at Douglas had instituted a ten-grade curriculum and, at sixteen, he was a member of its first graduating class.

"I thought at that time that I would probably be a farmer," Dr. Davidson explained, "so my family all encouraged me to prepare for the full course in agriculture at the State University in Lincoln instead of following the others to Peru." But first he would have to work.

Nebraska farms had recently met some severe summers with hot winds that parched vegetation and caused crop failures, though nothing like the crop devastations which had occurred some years earlier. Three times in the six years preceding Lee's birth, Rocky Mountain locusts, in swarms so thick and so vast that the sun was actually darkened as in Biblical stories, descended upon thousands of acres of Nebraska's ripening grain fields and completely ruined the crops. The Davidson farm had been in a section which escaped these visitations. Now, too, in the years following Lee's graduation from the Douglas school when he was farming as a full-time occupation, things went well on the farm. One winter he went up to Lincoln for work in agriculture at the State University, available for those who did not have enough credits to enroll as freshmen. With the credits he earned that winter, plus success in college entrance examinations prepared for by home study, plus some money saved, he was ready for and able to enter the University when he was twenty.

By this time farm machinery unquestionably interested

him more than farming. So he entered the Engineering School of the University to work for a degree in mechanical engineering. During summer vacations he worked as a machinist in locomotive shops. Engines—especially internal combustion engines—had become his main interest. Back at the University after a summer job, instead of designing the cornpicker he had been thinking about, he and a fellow student, Leon W. Chase, designed and built a five-horsepower engine. In his senior year he was student assistant in the University shops. He was a busy man that year, but not too busy to see something of a fellow student, Jennie Baldridge, whom he later married.

The more he worked with machines—especially gas engines—the better he liked it. Gas engineering attracted him most. When a job was offered him, as his graduation was approaching in the spring of 1904, in the experimental department of a Wisconsin engine manufacturing concern, he was glad to accept it.

That summer, unsolicited on "J.B.'s" part, the offer came which changed the way, though possibly not the fundamental direction of his lifework. The University of Nebraska had built a new laboratory, was instituting additional courses in a field designated as "Farm Mechanics," and asked him to teach them. On thinking it over, Davidson came to the conclusion that a position in a state university might offer greater opportunity to contribute to the development of agricultural machinery than would a job in industry. His boyhood dream of helping make better agricultural equipment was still with him though he could not see clearly just how it could best be achieved. Faced with need for a decision now, something urged him toward a state university which was trying, as Nebraska State was, to serve both agriculture and engineering. So he came to his decision, asked to be released from the job on which he was working, and returned to Nebraska as an instructor.

The courses in Farm Mechanics were very practical as he presented them that year. The only available textbook on the subject was an English book written before labor-saving machinery had been introduced generally into farm work. Obviously this could be no help. But technical and farm journals of the day were carrying up-to-the-minute material and J.B. had had enough actual experience in the mechanics essential to farming to come through his first year as a college instructor well enough to have Iowa State College offer him an assistant professorship in what was now beginning to be visualized as agricultural engineering.

At Iowa State, Davidson's main job would now be to train teachers to give such courses as he himself had just been teaching. A spontaneous demand was arising throughout the Middle West for courses on farm mechanics, the reason for which can easily be understood by looking at a few figures on farm machinery sales in America in these years. In 1903—the year before Davidson had come out of college—fifteen tractors had been manufactured in America. The year he went to Iowa State several hundred were manufactured and the numbers were beginning to multiply rapidly. By 1910, four thousand, and by 1920, more than two hundred thousand tractors had been manufactured. (About four million tractors were in use on American farms in 1950.) Other mechanical equipment sales were increasing in somewhat similar proportions, and our Middle West, where most of the early mechanized equipment found its greatest sale, quite naturally witnessed a spontaneous demand for courses in farm mechanics.

State colleges and universities did their best to meet this demand. Davidson did his best to meet it, too, not only in his teaching but in preparing a suitable textbook which could be used wherever courses in farm mechanics were instituted. From published material and from personal experience he and Leon Chase, friend of student days, collaborated in gathering and systematizing available knowledge on farm machinery. They went to factories to see the machines as they were being built and tested, and then went out to see them in action on farms. *Farm Machinery and Farm Motors*, with drawings and photographs, was published in 1908 in both the United States and England, and became invaluable to farmers already using or planning to use mechanized equipment as well as in the classroom.

And now, with Mr. Davidson as a strong factor and the wholehearted cooperation of Dean Anson Marston of the Engineering Division, and Dean Charles F. Curtiss of the Division of Agriculture, Iowa State began to expand its engineering curriculum by instituting a four-year course leading to a bachelor's degree in agricultural engineering. Throughout the Middle West the idea had germinated that a "marriage" between agriculture and engineering, similar to that already existing between mining and engineering, suggested such advantages for agriculture that it should be encouraged. Davidson himself had already issued the call which had resulted (in 1907) in the organization meeting of the American Society of Agricultural Engineers with sixteen men in attendance, and was serving as its first president. Along with a few others he was trying to visualize the educational needs of a branch of engineering in which farm mechanics would occupy the same place mechanics occupied in mechanical or mining engineering, while its whole curriculum would serve the whole of agriculture. No one knew exactly how the new curriculum would best be built but, as Davidson saw it, agricultural engineering at Iowa State would be a curriculum within the engineering school, with the school of agriculture cooperating. The degree would be fundamentally an engineering degree.

It would be a good many years before this group of pioneers and others who joined them would achieve the type of curriculum which would best fulfill their many-sided vision. Davidson steadily maintained that, as engineers, the main interests of the new group must be the main interests of all engineers: (1) labor efficiency, (2) economical application of power, or energy, and (3) the best use of materials. Obviously his own primary interest—the development of better farm machines and equipment—would be of importance. But farm structures, rural electrification, and soil and water conservation through drainage, irrigation, erosion control, etc., were agricultural engineering problems of high importance, too. The fact that the new engineers would have to serve six million individual farm units, most of them small units, created new types of problems for the educators—as did the fact that the agricultural engineer would also have to understand how to work with living, organic materials (soils, plants, and animals) rather than only with the inorganic materials with which most engineering dealt. This latter fact, incidentally, has always meant that farm life is an excellent background for a student to bring to agricultural engineering.

The new curriculum got under way at Iowa State and one by one other state colleges, with Nebraska in the forefront, led by Engineering Dean Stout and Dean Richards of the Agricultural Division, established curricula leading to degrees similar to Iowa State's B.S.A.E. For a considerable period Mr. Davidson's graduates headed the work in practically all of them. Today his graduates are still heads of departments in a great number of the American and Canadian institutions educating agricultural engineers, while graduate students from Europe and Asia, attracted to Iowa State by Dr. Davidson's special courses and high reputation, carry on his work in their native lands.

Important though his training of teachers has been, other aspects of Davidson's work surely have equal importance. For one thing, Iowa State College had an excellent Agricultural Experiment Station, and extension services in both agriculture and engineering. With Davidson's new department functioning, stress was put on the engineering approach to some of the state's problems in agriculture. To serve the farmers of Iowa, much work at its State College had to be at an individual farm unit level, and this level had importance to an engineer like Davidson. Iowa had some two hundred thousand farms. How and where could cow barns, chicken houses and pigpens be built on these farms so they could be kept in proper sanitary condition in the most economical way? What materials for construction offered best economies in the end? Questions like these could be solved best by men with knowledge in structural and sanitary engineering, and who were familiar with specific conditions prevailing on Iowa farms.

Davidson himself became the author, or co-author, of more than thirty bulletins issued by the Iowa Agricultural Experiment Station, and though his specialty was power machinery and its problems, some of his papers were on hog and poultry houses, concrete blocks for farm construction, concrete fence posts and septic tanks. None of the engineering problems touching Iowa farms were too small to warrant engineer attention, because results meant economies and higher standards of living for millions of human beings. Not only in the Station's bulletins but in farm magazines Davidson recorded, in terms understandable to the farmer, facets of progress applicable to the home farm.

In the field of his main interest—power machinery—Davidson kept in mind, too, the needs of the individual farm. As he saw it, two main things were to be achieved by farm machinery: the reduction of human drudgery and a far more plentiful food supply. Since not more than one farm in every ten of our six million farm units exceeded 250 or 260 acres, the need for the type of machinery which could be afforded on smaller farms was quite as great as for the more expensive machinery for harvesting on a vast scale. The application of gas engines to small equipment had many problems to be ironed out before small farms could be satisfactorily served. Important papers appeared over Davidson's name in journals interested in these problems. He was one of the men whose advice was constantly sought by manufacturers making power machinery for farm use. He served as a manufacturer's consultant on farm equipment for years after his retirement at Iowa State.

Machines were common on Iowa farms, to be sure, before Davidson was of an age to step into the picture as an engineer. The percentage of American workers engaged in agricultural pursuits had by that time dropped from eighty-five to approximately thirty-five. But the great increase in the use of machinery did not arrive until gasoline-powered machines replaced horse- or mule-powered machines. Davidson's main contribution was of the gas engine era. His books—he had another by this time, covering the field of agricultural engineering—his papers and studies became of increasing importance when the effects of World War I began to be felt. Men who had once been available for farm work now flocked to war industries, and simultaneously our farms had to meet the need of feeding extra millions of hungry people in Europe who were soon to be our active Allies. To meet this problem, in Iowa as in every other agricultural state thousands of fertile acres had to be planted and reaped to feed horses and mules, and the only way to grow more food for Europe was to raise and feed more horses and mules. American factories were too busy with munitions, tanks and airplanes to turn to farm equipment on the scale on which it was now needed.

When the war was over a decrease in the number of horses and mules on American farms began to take place. Some idea of what happened in the comparatively few years between the end of World War I and America's entry into World War II is evident in a few figures. In 1920, more than twenty-six million horses and mules were in use on our farms. Fewer than half that number were in use during the World War II period when our farms produced food which fed fifty million more people than during the World War I period. And the percentage of our workers employed in agriculture had dropped to fifteen per cent of our total workers! Agricultural engineering production techniques had not only improved the wellbeing of the farmer, but had released millions of workers for the production of other services and commodities which have contributed to the wellbeing of all people.

To state exactly Dr. Davidson's part in all this is impossible. But it is accurate to say that Iowa was well in the forefront of this achievement and Davidson was well in the forefront of what was happening in Iowa. Part of what he accomplished was through his work with the American Society of Agricultural Engineers. This Society was a power in bringing electrification to many rural districts, and without electrification much mechanization would have been retarded—modern poultry and dairy farms, for example, and the use of labor-saving devices which have removed much drudgery from the farm home. A more personal achievement—one with nation-wide results—was his survey of farm equipment in 1926, made under the auspices of the United States Department of Agriculture in cooperation with the National Association of Farm Equipment Manufacturers. His third book, *Agricultural Machinery*, published in 1931, and his editorship of the John Wiley series of books on agricultural engineering, have been genuine contributions which have made available much information needed by those interested in the industry and the engineering problems of agriculture.

Certainly Davidson had a great deal to do with the engineering features back of Iowa's success with its main crop, corn. For many years he conducted tests and other work which applied engineering methods in the growing and harvesting of corn. Since one of the engineer's main interests in any industry is prevention of waste, one of the problems that interested Davidson about corn as a source of Iowa farm incomes as well as of national food supply was prevention of waste of the stalks. Chemists had shown that the cellulose in these stalks had economic value—in the making of paper, for example—and as an engineer Davidson knew the difference between profit and loss in an industry often depends upon the use made of what were once thought of as waste products. To prevent waste of corn stalks, machinery was needed for gathering them economically in the fields, for baling them, separating the inedible from the edible parts the farmer can use on his farm, processing and storing the parts he can use and delivering the rest to a manufacturer located in a spot where he can pay a price profitable to himself as well as to the farmer. Into these and other facets of corn production Dr. Davidson put efforts that produced results. Statistics in the 1940's showed that the use of engineering methods were enabling some Iowa farmers to produce corn at the rate of one bushel for every four minutes of human labor, while at the same time as much as five hundred minutes of human labor were being used, per bushel of corn, in some sections of our country.

Twice in his life Dr. Davidson was sent to foreign countries—first to Russia and later to China—to contribute to better agricultural practices. In 1929 he became a member of an American Commission to the USSR where, he said, "to be an American engineer was, at that time, to be esteemed, but to be an American agricultural engineer was to hold a place of special honor." He believed that the application of engineering techniques to agriculture under the first five-year plan was primarily responsible for Russia's ability to withstand the Nazis in World War II. The work of American engineers in Russia in this period was effective in sowing seeds of friendship and respect between individual human beings of the two nations, and many believe it is one of the indestructible factors that will eventually result in a lasting peace among the nations of the world.

In 1947, after his services as consultant to the War Production Board and to the U.S. Relief and Rehabilitation Administration were over and his retirement age at Iowa State had been reached, Dr. Davidson became chairman of a four-man Committee on Agricultural Engineering for China. This committee was under appointment from the Minister of Agriculture and Forestry of the Republic of China and was sponsored by more than a score of American firms manufacturing farm equipment. Because of primitive agricultural methods China was a land of starvation, although eighty per cent of its people were engaged in agriculture. The committee's job was tremendous. Under the Chinese Republic's Ministry of Agriculture and Forestry the four Americans were to cooperate in a seven-year program which envisaged, among other things: the strengthening of the agricultural engineering department of the College of Agriculture of Nanking University; establishing two such departments at existing colleges of agriculture; selection of a group of Chinese college graduates for at least three years of study in agricultural engineering in the United States who were to return to positions of leadership in the field in China; division of China into twelve regions in which twelve agricultural experiment stations were immediately to be set up, with twelve national agricultural colleges to follow eventually; and establishing manufacturing concerns in China which could turn out the tools and machines necessary for modern agricultural methods in China.

After two years the committee had to leave China because of Communist control in the areas in which it had been working. But much had been accomplished which meant steps forward in reducing starvation in Asia.

Dr. Davidson's fellow engineers honored him with the Cyrus Hall McCormick Medal for exceptional and meritorious achievement in agriculture. He received Estranger membership in the Royal Agricultural Society of Sweden and other honors. Like all good teachers, though, he felt the work of his students here and abroad was the most vital part of his contribution to the profession he helped bring to birth. At the time of his death in 1957 not only were they filling some highly important positions in the academic world and in the experiment stations of state colleges of agriculture, but they are to be found in scores of jobs within the U.S. Department of Agriculture where the engineering approach is a recognized asset. They are to be found in soil erosion work which has achieved much since the dust storms of the 1930's, in rural electrification work and the new types of jobs which followed in the wake of rural electrification—ultra-violet lighting to increase egg production, farm food dehydration, electric blowing for cooling and curing hay and grain on individual farms, etc.

They are to be found, of course, in the industries which design and manufacture power machinery for farms. Others are engaged in the engineering organizations which specialize in work to replace rundown, obsolete farm structures with modern structures which supply heat and moisture protection, drainage, and all other engineering features needed for the best structural care of America's food supply, both plant and animal. In short, everywhere agricultural engineers are performing a job today, Davidson's students are likely to be found, helping not only to perform it but to improve existing engineering methods for performing it.

Harold Bright Maynard

(1902 –   )

INDUSTRIAL ENGINEERING CONSULTANT,
PRESIDENT OF THE METHODS ENGINEERING
COUNCIL WHICH SPECIALIZES ON MANAGE-
MENT PROBLEMS IN INDUSTRY

□□□□□□□□□□□□□□□□□□□□□□□□□□□□□□

WHEN Mike Maynard
went to Cornell in the fall of 1919 it was a toss-up whether
he preferred engineering to agriculture or agriculture to
engineering. It would be one or the other—there was little
question about that. He had refused a four-year scholarship at Harvard because it did not offer this choice of work,
and selected a university which had both agricultural and
engineering colleges. Faced with need for a decision between the two when he registered, a vague preference for
engineering made him choose the school of engineering.
But it was with the thought that he could transfer to agriculture if he found he had made a mistake.

Refusing the Harvard scholarship had not been a decision
to make lightly. Harold Maynard's father had died when
he was seven, and his mother had undertaken to support
herself and two children by teaching. They moved from

Northampton, Massachusetts, where Harold had been born, to Philadelphia where Mrs. Maynard taught science in a private school for girls. Within a few months the younger child died and Harold and his education became his mother's consuming interest outside her teaching. She put her son in private schools in first grade and, despite the financial burden, kept him there until he was ready for college because she was convinced he would get a better education in private schools than in public schools available. Mike's marks in his last three pre-college years at the Protestant Episcopal Academy earned a scholarship for him and he avoided some of the expensive social activities of his classmates. The quality of education available at the Academy was worth a few sacrifices to both Maynards.

So, when it came time for the decision about the Harvard scholarship, Mike's natural approach was not only from the financial standpoint but to ask the question: "Will Harvard give me the kind of education I need for what I want to do with my life?" Knowing by this time that farming or engineering was what he felt most desire for, and that he was apparently qualified to prepare for either type of work, the answer to the question was negative and he refused the scholarship.

Why does one sixteen-year-old youth know so definitely what he wants to do that he can refuse an opportunity like this and never regret it, while others flounder about for years blowing hot and cold on whether they want to do this or that as a life work? In Mike Maynard no unique talent had urged itself forward such as enabled Vannevar Bush, at sixteen, to be working successfully with radio before many engineers knew much about it. If heredity and environment had anything to do with making Maynard reject an arts course even though he was vague about technology courses, he thinks they probably came through his grandfather. C. A. Maynard and Company was a well-established shovel manufacturing concern in Northampton when Mike was born. It was owned by his grandfather who successfully combined in his own life a love of agriculture with manufacturing interests. A "gentleman farmer," they called him in New England, because farming was his avocation as he earned his living by other means. It was a pattern which made strong appeal to the grandson.

Among Mike's earliest memories are some of himself as a very small boy watching, with a feeling of fascination he could recall vividly as a grown man, the drop-forge hammers with which workmen were fashioning shovels in his grandfather's plant. He recalls, too, the night when the fire alarm sounded and his grandfather's factory was in flames. Mike's father, then its superintendent, worked through the night with the firemen and came home wet, cold, and exhausted. Pneumonia developed, he died, and his young widow, graduated from Smith College recently enough to be qualified to teach biology with very little brushing up, decided upon the move to Philadelphia which meant that Mike would be out of touch with the rebuilt factory except during vacation periods.

Those summers back in Northampton were fun. They were also work. The Maynards were one of the New England families who believed in work as well as play for growing boys. Mike had a job in his grandfather's factory painting trowel handles one summer. No spray painting in those days! Mike and his brush earned something like a cent per handle. Helping in the garden had always been fun, but when Mike was of a size and age for it he had his own vegetable garden from which he had to earn his own spending money. This was work as well as fun. When he wanted a saxophone his family said, "Fine. Earn it!" He did, and they did not complain too much about the noise. Year by year he learned the relationship between work and money and pleasure and he thinks it was a good experience.

He was not quite seventeen when he entered Cornell and there his vagueness about engineering began to clarify. Doubtless it would have clarified more quickly if the type of courses in industrial engineering, or management, had been available then as now. This was definitely the type of engineering in which Maynard's talents lay. But, of scores of engineering colleges in the United States in 1919, not more than six or eight had instituted management courses (or industrial engineering, or engineering administration, as the courses were variously called) and only a few others had as yet introduced management subjects into their mechanical engineering curriculum.

For the thousands of young men interested in the management of industry as their future field of work, this period when Mike Maynard entered college was of great importance. The term "management," universally used now, was scarcely used at all then. If a young man wanted to prepare in college for "top boss jobs" in industry, he went to such institutions as the Wharton School of Business and Finance or to Harvard's Graduate School for Business Administration—as many still do. Engineering education and experience were not considered necessary, or even desirable, often, for running an industry, and engineers rarely rose to the higher administrative levels.

Part of the reason for this was that engineering schools had not provided a broad enough curriculum to fit engineers adequately for top-level jobs. When Maynard entered Cornell a handful of engineering educators were beginning to face this problem more squarely. The value of mechanical engineering education and experience in top jobs had become too obvious to be denied in meeting World War I's production problems, and educators were beginning to accept responsibility for training young engineers for a bigger part in industrial management.

Luckily for Maynard, Dexter I. Kimball, Dean of Cornell's Sibley College of Engineering (who always kept a hand in engineering work outside academic halls as well as within them) was one of the early engineering educators to recognize (1) need for the engineering mind at the management level in industry and (2) the academic importance of training engineers better for such jobs. Cornell had no industrial engineering course leading to a degree, but Dean Kimball had been one of the pioneers in introducing management subjects into the mechanical engineering curriculum. So when Maynard registered that fall he became one of some ten or eleven thousand students registered for a degree in mechanical engineering in our engineering colleges that year rather than one of only a few hundred registered in the new industrial engineering courses offered at the Massachusetts Institute of Technology, Penn State, Sheffield at Yale, Purdue and several other colleges.

More than half who entered as engineering freshmen that year would flunk out or drop out but Maynard was in no danger of being one of them so far as flunking was concerned. He was still in danger—if it could be called a danger—of dropping out because closer acquaintanceship with engineering might reveal his preference for agriculture. Quite the contrary happened. When he got his teeth into some of the new industrial engineering courses all thought of transferring to agriculture left him. Moments began to arrive when he experienced the feeling of fascination in some industrial engineering problem which he had experienced as a boy watching men at work in his grandfather's factory.

Far from wanting to transfer to agriculture, Maynard admits he practically "ate 'em alive" when he got his teeth into industrial engineering subjects. In his senior year he decided there was one immediate spot in industry he wanted more than any other. The Westinghouse Electric

Corporation had a one-year works management course for which ten or twelve qualified engineering graduates were selected each year. Maynard wanted that course and he asked for it. When the Westinghouse representative came to the campus as usual that spring Maynard was one of the seniors interviewed, and before his commencement day arrived a letter came asking him to report in Pittsburgh that fall. Interpreting the invitation to mean he had been accepted for the course, and well pleased with his prospects, Maynard bought himself a motor cycle, put it on board a boat and sailed with a friend to spend the summer touring Europe just for the fun of it.

In September he went to Pittsburgh. To his surprise the Westinghouse executive to whom he reported told him that, although he was in the group *suggested* for the works management course, final selection of the young men to be accepted now rested with him. Westinghouse had openings for many young engineers, he continued, who could not be accepted for this very limited course, and he now wanted to ask Maynard the questions which would reveal his qualifications as they might best fit the Westinghouse needs and opportunities.

Maynard answered the questions, and finally the last one was reached.

"What would you yourself prefer," his interrogator said, "if you do not happen to be one of the few accepted for the works management course?"

Maynard looked at his watch.

"There's a train back to New England in about two hours," he said. "I'd have just about enough time to catch it."

Whereupon it turned out there would be no need to catch the train. Mike put on work clothes, instead, and went to work in the shops, and in due time moved on to other departments—time study, inventory control, production control, accounting, cost department, and so on. In each spot he rubbed elbows with the other workers for a period that might vary from two weeks to two months, seeing the job from the worker's viewpoint everywhere before he would have opportunity to see it from even a minor position at any management angle.

The year passed, and of all the work Maynard had seen and helped perform, time study had interested him most. He stated his preference at the end of the year and was assigned to work with Gustav Stegemerten, head of the rate setting department of the Controller Division in which time studies were made. Unknowingly he was headed toward the methods engineering work which became his life work. In trying to improve time studies Maynard recognized the importance of methods of work—not only methods used by time study men but methods used by workers on jobs being time-studied. He saw that studies of *how* work ought to be done were of as much importance as studies of *how long it took to do the work*—in most cases of greater importance. Out of his recognition of this fact grew his Methods Engineering Council.

To begin at the beginning: Time studies at Westinghouse as Maynard met them when he was twenty-one were pretty much what they were in any well-run plant in the electrical industry of that day. Their object was to establish accurate time standards upon which to base wage rates. As everyone knows, labor costs are an important item in determining a product's selling price. At best, then, wage rates should (1) enable a man to earn wages that are fair when judged by American standards of living in his community, and (2) enable the company paying them to compete fairly with other companies upholding American standards and fair business practices. High skills should have due reward; wage rates should be an incentive for all workers to do the best day's work of which they are individually capable, without harm to their health. Time studies for determining wage rates had many advantages for honest worker and honest employer; but because of old abuses by unscrupulous workers and employers alike, wage-rate systems which stimulated worker production had always been a bone of contention in industry.

Maynard's immediate job was to help determine a normal day's work, through fair time studies, for any job he studied. This is harder to do than the inexperienced realize. Worker fatigue and other human factors must be taken into account, and Maynard soon learned that human beings have more variables than Vannevar Bush's differential analyzer had to deal with in its mathematical equations up to eighteen variables. Psychological factors enter into time studies to throw a monkey wrench into the most honest calculations.

Like Stegemerten and others he recognized how much the psychological element within the time-study men themselves could enter into their results. For example, when a rate was to be set for a certain operation, how many men should be studied in order to obtain the fairest results when applied to all workers? Also, *which* men should be timed— the most highly skilled and the least highly skilled, or a group of average workers, or a mixture of all? Suppose the time-study man decided to study five men (personal opinion entered into the number five) and that A, D, J, R, and Z (personal selection entered into these decisions, too), were to represent highly, moderately, and poorly skilled workers. Would adding up the minutes it took each of these men to do a job, and dividing by five, really be the time it should take an average worker to do the job? It was a little like the method of arriving at the average income of all salesmen in a concern by selecting five men of high, moderate, and low selling ability, finding their total yearly incomes amount to $30,000 per year and saying the average salesman has $6,000 per year to live on. Actually only one man in the whole five is earning as much as that if their respective incomes are $12,000, $5,000, $5,000, $4,500, and $3,500.

Or, take another angle in time-study work as Maynard was meeting it. Personal elements enter into the rating of skills just as they enter into rating examination papers. Some teachers rarely give an A, others give A to half the class. How can a worker's skills be rated equitably for all, or the skill of one operation compared fairly with the skill of another operation when human judgments enter into the ratings?

These were a few of the things Maynard was puzzling about, especially as they applied to methods he and Stegemerten were using in making time studies. Progress was made in eliminating some of the personal factors, and continued after Stegemerten was advanced and Maynard became rate supervisor. Procedures were becoming somewhat more scientific. Then Maynard was sent to the South Philadelphia Westinghouse works to develop time studies and wage incentive practices there.

Here, as supervisor of methods and equipment, he found another impetus to the methods work in which he would later excel. He learned the hard way—that is, by being forced to do it the wrong way—that the most satisfactory way to install good methods is before workers are trained to poor methods. Suspicion was always roused by studies that aimed at increased production through better methods even if they meant fatter pay envelopes for some workers—and rightly so when one realizes how often in the past such studies had resulted in loss of jobs for other workers. But Maynard won confidence as he worked with shop committees representing the workers (the electrical industry had not yet been unionized) and succeeded so well that he became superintendent of production for the whole South

Philadelphia works while he was still in his twenties.

Then came the depression and for Maynard it became a time for a decision. Was he going to spend his life working for other people or was he going to work for himself? One of the strong pulls toward agriculture had been that a farmer is his own boss. He had known he could reach that goal in engineering if he could become a consultant. He now had six years of industrial experience to qualify him for such a step. Industry was beginning to recognize greater need for time study, and very few trained time study men were available. Industries would have to train their own men which would create need for consultants in this field. Maynard's experience qualified him as a specialist here.

Yet he was not quite ready to hang out his shingle as a consultant. For six years he had amassed time-study records without time to digest them thoroughly. He felt sure that proper analysis and study of these records would reveal hidden meanings, produce something of scientific value. It was a perilous time to give up a job. Nevertheless, this is what he did and, with his wife and a mass of time-study material, went abroad where it was cheaper to live than in America, and spent a year analyzing and studying his records as he enlarged his engineering and cultural background. Also he put in some work that year developing his skill as a writer. He had already been one of the authors of a book presenting that part of the time-study material that had been ready for presentation. Now his aim was to be able to write well enough to give his ideas as wide an audience as possible. Maynard was not going to become one of the professional men who keep their methods secret, to be used for their own personal advantage, and their clients', only.

It all worked as planned until he came back to Philadelphia in 1931 and, fitting up an office in his home, hung out his shingle as a consulting engineer specializing in time study and methods. No clients appeared. He waited, as patiently as he could, one year, two years, until it was apparent that his mousetrap was not baited with a cheese of sufficient power to attract the clients he had to have.

Yet he was convinced he had something they would want if they knew about it. True, the years were those of the early 1930's and the depression had witnessed the failure of hundreds of concerns which might otherwise have been numbered among potential clients. Industry was cutting every possible expense. Nevertheless, many an industry still in existence needed better methods if it was to be able to survive. So Maynard's first problem was largely one of how to make prospective clients aware of what his time study and methods work could do for them.

He and Stegemerten had continued their friendship and work interests over the years and, in talking over Maynard's problem of how to attract clients for the new engineering specialty he had to offer, they hit upon the phrase (new, so far as either knew), "methods engineering." From this, the name "Methods Engineering Council" was coined to state exactly what Maynard could offer clients. He now moved to Pittsburgh, took space in an office building in Wilkinsburg, and sent out announcements of the services of the Methods Engineering Council. The year was 1934 and Maynard had been without salary for four years. He continued to be without what most engineers would call salary for another two years. It gave him a certain confidence that he continued to have offers to re-enter industry on a salary basis. He refused as he had refused the Harvard scholarship because it did not offer what he wanted most.

By 1935 clients began to come. Westinghouse was one of the first. Before long Maynard's one-man Council became a two- and then a three-engineer concern. Why?

Because Mike Maynard had something valuable to offer and satisfied clients brought new clients. It had been tough getting started but not so tough once the ball started rolling. Four-fifths of the Council's new contracts through the years have come through earlier clients. By 1950 its staff, in addition to clerical and secretarial workers, numbered fifty professional and technical specialists in practically every phase of management work. It was occupying a complete building in Wilkinsburg providing offices, a modern research laboratory, conference rooms, an auditorium used as a training center, and a research library. It was recognized as one of the outstanding consultant groups in America and had a considerable clientele in Europe.

Several things in Maynard's work are unusual. One is the training division which conducts special training courses, in the home building, for personnel selected by clients. Maynard believes *show-how* is as important as *know-how* in engineering. The aim of the training courses is to show how his own organization's know-how may become the permanent possession of a client. But possibly the most unusual contribution his work has helped make to industrial engineering is, as may be expected, the "methods-time-measurement" work, as it eventually came to be called, which grew out of the earlier time-study work with Stegemerten.

Maynard had had new stimulus to the old problem of setting standards for a fair day's work when his methods improvement program for Westinghouse made savings of $600,000 a year in direct labor costs, but brought new industrial relations problems every time he had to ask workers to accept improved methods. Obviously, the engineering consultant would have to continue to do this "methods correction" work, and the challenge was to find an objectively scientific way to set work standards so that, when changes were made, workers would know the new standards were as free as possible from errors of human judgment. But as Maynard saw it, the great challenge was to find how methods could best be studied *before* a job was put into production. If workers could be taught the best way first, countless problems in human relations in industry could be avoided. So it was methods engineering more than methods correction that was his first interest and aim.

Like some of the other time-study men of this period he had come to recognize the scientific importance of Frank Gilbreth's motion-study work of twenty years earlier. Gilbreth's techniques for discovering better work methods included motion pictures of workers performing a job, from which analysis of all motions was made for the purpose of discovering how to eliminate unnecessary motions. To do this scientifically Gilbreth had conceived the idea of analyzing all movement into fundamental motion elements (select; grasp; transport, loaded; release; transport, empty; etc.) which he called "therbligs." That work had been in a pioneer stage when Gilbreth died, but Lillian Gilbreth, his wife and co-worker, had trained a group of younger men in her husband's methods and by the early 1930's motion-study courses were in some of the engineering colleges.

Maynard and Stegemerten now teamed up to put their time studies on a more scientific basis by incorporating scientific motion study into them. They selected drill press operation for study. They took motion pictures of work done on these presses and, from study of the films, calculated a standard time for the performance of each motion element—with measurement when called for (as in distance covered in transport, loaded and empty). If their method and work were correct, any drill-press operation anywhere would be divisible into these motion elements and, by adding standard times of all motion elements constituting any

piece of drill-press work, a standard time for its performance could be reached. Test of the validity of both
method and work would be made by comparing this
standard time with the time being consumed in actual practice in shops in the Pittsburgh district.

A young Westinghouse employee, John L. Schwab, had
come into the project and accompanied Maynard to the
shop selected for the first test. Watching a drill-press operator they would identify the succession of motion elements
he used in his particular operation, then add up their pre-
calculated standard times for all the elements and see if
the total checked with the time actually used on this
operation.

A blow seemed to fall when they found they could not
make the test because the work as it was being done in this
shop could not be subdivided into the motion elements for
which standard times had been calculated. The idea came
that if their standard time data were broken down more
finely, they would cover the motions being used in this first
shop. Once this was done the time standards developed
from the original research work checked almost perfectly
with the time consumed in actual practice in the first shop.
They checked just as accurately in the next ten shops, and
then in another ten!

The possibilities were certainly exciting. If jobs were
selected for filming which contained *all* elements of motions, and if standard times for each motion element were
accurately collated into tables, thousands of jobs could be
timed by the tables derived from the study of a few well-
selected jobs. If proper allowances for unavoidable delays
and worker fatigue were incorporated into the tabulated
results, a trained man could walk into a plant, watch an
operation, and calculate the time it should take and what a
normal day's work on this job should be. More than that,
since motions in manual operations all analyzed into identi-

cal motion elements, the tables could be applied for arriving at standard times for lathe operations, punch-press operation and any other manual operation without even filming it. There seemed to be no reason why hard work and intelligence could not accomplish this, and Stegemerten and Schwab both left Westinghouse to join the Methods Engineering Council. That was in 1946 and there seems to be no question but that methods-time-measurement is a success. Eventually, standard basic elements were worked out which minimized the work of applying the methods-time-measurement procedure. The methods engineer learns to use these basic elements to build effective methods just as the high school student learns to form useful chemical compounds by combining chemical elements in various ways.

Though very close to Harold Maynard's heart, methods-time-measurement is only one part of the work of the Methods Engineering Council. His whole professional aim is, as he expresses it, "to make the Methods Engineering Council the best-thought-of management group in the world," with methods-time-measurement as one of its specialized techniques. With this in mind, MEC expanded during the 1950's till the scope of its services covered practically all phases of management activity. By 1957 its staff had more than double the fifty professional and technical specialists it had numbered in 1950.

This expansion does not mean that Maynard's aim is to have the Methods Engineering Council become the biggest or most successful management group in the world. He wants it to help perform a world service by enabling industry to contribute more and more greatly to the betterment of all men everywhere. He is deeply convinced that scientific management has something vital to offer in the solution of world problems. He believes that if industry constantly shows the value of better management practices which stabilize high production and improve human relations, governments will eventually use scientific management in ways that will stabilize domestic and foreign affairs and improve international relations. He believes that greater acceptance of the ideals and techniques of scientific management will enable all men in all nations to share more rapidly in the abundance science and technology make possible, as they achieve better human relationships with each other.

Recognition of Mr. Maynard's contributions to his profession has been made by national and international management groups alike who have called him to high office in their organizations. The Gilbreth and Melville medals have been awarded him, as has the Wallace Clark Award for outstanding contributions to management in the international field. He holds an honorary doctorate from the University of Miami.

8

Ole Singstad

(1882 —   )

NORWEGIAN-BORN AND NORWEGIAN-EDU-
CATED AMERICAN CIVIL ENGINEER, DE-
SIGNER OF THE HOLLAND TUNNEL AND
ITS VENTILATING SYSTEM, WHO BECAME
THE WORLD'S GREATEST AUTHORITY ON
VEHICULAR TUNNELS

■□■□■□■□■□■□■□■□■□■□■□■□■□■□

ONE reason why a young
civil engineering graduate by the name of Ole (pronounced
Ō′ lē) Singstad came to America in 1905 was because he
thought he might find more opportunity here than in Norway. Another reason was an urge to see more of the
world. "Maybe my Viking ancestors had something to do
with my coming," he says. "They always wanted to see
'what lies on the other side of the mountain' and so did I."

Ole Singstad was by no means certain that he wanted to
remain in America that day he stepped off the boat. But
he remained, and he found engineering opportunities he
could not possibly have found in his homeland. Conditions
which gave rise to his type of engineering achievement did
not exist in Norway. Singstad's opportunity arose out of
the need of a vast metropolitan center to solve some of its

traffic congestion problems. These problems had arisen because several times as many people had crowded into a
few hundred square miles around New York Harbor as
live, even yet, in all of Norway's 125,000 square miles.

New York City's traffic problems were intensified beyond those of most cities because Manhattan, its business
center, is an island. Originally it was accessible only by
boat or, later, by bridge. Eventually, access by underground and underwater electric railways was achieved.
With the advent of mass production of automobiles, bridges
proved inadequate for motor traffic, and long underwater
tunnels for the use of automobiles throwing off poisonous
gases offered complex problems in ventilation that had
never been met before. These problems were solved mainly
by an engineer who had never seen America until he was
twenty-three.

How did it happen that, of all the engineers in America,
Ole Singstad was the one to become the world's greatest
authority on vehicular tunnels? As a boy he had nothing
to make him think or dream about either tunnels or traffic
problems. Born on a farm in the small rural community of
Lensvik, near Trondheim, Norway, on June 29, 1882, Ole's
early life was spent in an environment where the highest
point of his traffic experience must have been achieved in
keeping out of the way of other children on skates and bobsleds. The elementary school he attended until he was in
his teens was the distance of only a city block or two from
his home. There was no need for his mother to worry
about traffic as she muffled up the young Singstads—nine of
them, eventually—for the short trip to school, even though
the children had to go to school in the dark during Lensvik's long winter.

In summer vacation time Ole and his playmates had
miles of grazing land and timber land to roam through, in
the narrow plain between the Singstad farm and the long

mountain range that traverses the length of Norway—those mountains that Ole's Viking ancestors traditionally wanted to see over. There were lakes, too, on his father's land and that of friendly neighboring farmers. In these fresh-water lakes and rivers Ole first learned the art of trout fishing which became his lifelong recreation in America. Darkness never cut short those summer vacation days, yet winter was not the combination of darkness and bitter cold many Americans associate with a locality lying as near the Arctic Circle as Trondheim. The Gulf Stream along Norway's coast tempered the Lensvik climate throughout the year. The winters of Ole Singstad's youth were, though longer and darker, no more severe than many an American child of southern New England, Colorado, or even Ohio, experiences in a snappy American winter.

The length of the winter and the darkness were not without compensations for young Norwegians around Trondheim. Snow arrived in November and, because there were no great changes of climate during the winter months, it stayed on the ground until April. Norwegian children used their skates, their skis and their bobsleds for practically five months of every year. Ole became as adept at Norway's winter sports as he was at fishing, and some time in the course of his boyhood—on his way to a ski slope or a good fishing spot—he began to be increasingly aware of roads and bridges and that somebody had to build them. When he found himself thinking of himself as a man he often thought of making roads and building bridges. He knew definitely that he did not want to continue living on a farm. So the decision grew in him that he would study civil engineering.

Located in Trondheim was the Technical College which later became the Technological Institute of Trondheim. Since more students wanted to enter it each year than could be accepted, it had a waiting list. Excellence of preparation was a factor in gaining admittance and Ole Singstad attended both public and private secondary schools, with one year in college as preparation for studying civil engineering (*ingeniörvaesen*) at the Trondheim college. He was a good student, standing well up in the top group of his class without confining himself to the academic side of college life. He played on the college soccer team and served for a year as president of the Students' Society.

Like plenty of American students who keep a hand in extra-curricular college activities, Singstad learned how to "cram" occasionally at the last minute. The summer of his graduation he put off completing the drawings necessary in one of his engineering courses until the night before they were to be handed in. He remembers how he pulled his table over to the window of his room that evening and worked at his drafting board throughout the night without need to turn on the electric light. The drawings were handed in next morning, and in a few days he received his C.E. degree.

In deciding to come to America that same year (1905) Singstad was following the pattern of many Norwegians before him. In the preceding hundred years, out of a population that had never reached three million, one fourth that number of Norwegians had emigrated to the United States. In the more recent decades many had been young people from the professional groups who were conscious of limitations resulting from Norway's size, its difficult physical features and slowness in becoming industrialized. The United States had been the Land of Promise to Norwegians as much as to any group in Europe in the nineteenth century and they gave us one of our finest citizen groups. So now Ole Singstad decided he, too, would come to the United States long enough to find out whether he wanted to practice civil engineering here or in Norway.

He had to have a job, of course, in order to stay in

America long enough to know whether he wanted to stay permanently. He went to see an alumnus of his college who was a successful engineer here and through him found his first American job—transitman and bridge designer for the Central Railroad of New Jersey. Railroads were a good field for a young civil engineer. They suited Singstad and he soon began to feel very much at home in New York. Then a better job took him to Norfolk, Virginia, as designer and assistant engineer on construction of the Virginian Railroad. Here he designed railroad structures and assisted in rail and bridge construction. It was good, marketable American engineering experience and he stayed at it for three years. Then, as the building of the railroad was nearing completion, he resigned to return to New York where, he felt sure, some other opportunities awaited him. Before leaving Virginia he felt so at home that he decided to become an American citizen and took out his first papers.

Quite without premeditation Singstad now changed his work from railways and bridges to railways and tunnels. The Hudson River Tunnels of the Hudson-Manhattan Railway were nearing completion and "Merely by accident," he says, "I walked in on a job as a designing engineer with them." Except for a very brief period Ole Singstad has concentrated on underwater, or subaqueous tunnels ever since.

New York City was beginning, at this period, an extensive program of rapid-transit subway expansion which necessitated tunnels beneath New York and Brooklyn, and under the East River which separates them. Great advances in tunneling techniques had been made since that day in the early 1880's when the use of compressed air in the first Hudson River Tunnel work ever attempted had resulted in a break through the river bed above it which flooded the tunnel, caused the loss of twenty-three lives and temporary abandonment of the project. Before 1900 the joint use of compressed air with a tunnel shield (a technique originating with British engineers) had brought to successful completion two subaqueous tunnels—a water supply tunnel of ten-foot diameter under the Mersey River in England, and a railway tunnel twenty-one feet in diameter under the St. Clair River between the United States and Canada. This technique had finally mastered the abandoned Hudson River Tunnel which was completed as the McAdoo Tunnel in 1909, and put into use for rapid transit between New York City and New Jersey.

It was to the work on the New York City Rapid Transit subway system that Ole Singstad turned when his brief Hudson River Tunnel job came to an end. He was taken on as a designing engineer on the new subway tunnel projects and found the work extremely interesting. He felt at home in New York, and found the Public Service Commission of the First District of New York an excellent organization to work for. His job gave him opportunity to learn practically everything that was known about tunneling methods. But as year followed year there was one disadvantage which grew more and more irksome. Because his job was a Civil Service job, promotions had to follow Civil Service procedures. At the end of seven years he had achieved no promotion beyond that of being appointed chief of a squad of designing engineers, and each promotion would continue to be made mainly according to seniority of service.

"It seemed the only way I could get ahead," he says, "would be for some of my good friends and co-workers in Civil Service to die and make way for me." Regardless of ability, effort, and good work, promotions would depend largely upon whether one man had served two years, or maybe only two days, longer than the next man in line.

So in 1917, at the age of thirty-five, Ole Singstad took

what seemed to him to be the only way ahead at more than a snail's pace. Though he was now a married man with family responsibilities he left a job which was providing security and work he liked for what seemed to many a less secure future. There is a saying that a bird in the hand is worth two in the bush. In this instance Singstad preferred his chance with the birds in the bush. It led him temporarily away from tunnel design to other types of structural designing, but in a year he returned to his old field of work as planner and estimator on the Philadelphia rapid transit system and a proposed vehicular tunnel under the Delaware River.

Within another year the opportunity came which was to write Singstad's name into the history of tunneling in capital letters. Clifford Holland had been appointed chief engineer for a new type of tunnel project—a vehicular tunnel for automotive traffic between New Jersey and downtown New York. Knowing Singstad's work on New York subways where Holland himself had been a construction engineer, Holland now asked Singstad to become chief designing engineer for the new tunnel. Singstad hesitated. A tunnel built by two State Commissions sounded very much like the old Civil Service procedures.

"Think it over well," Holland suggested. "Good engineers, older than you, have applied for the job."

The conversation ended with Singstad saying he would talk it over with his wife before giving a definite answer.

He talked it over with Mrs. Singstad who said, "Well, why not? Why don't you do it?"

A few weeks later Ole Singstad boarded a ferry boat down near the Battery on his way up the Hudson for a little trout fishing before he tackled the most difficult job he had ever attempted. The boat approached Canal Street, the site of the New York end of the proposed new tunnel. He looked across the expanse of water to the Jersey side a mile away, and it is still hard for him to describe the feeling that flooded over him as he thought of designing a tunnel beneath so wide and deep a river bed, a tunnel which must pioneer in methods for handling the poisonous fumes of mass automobile traffic.

Even the layman can understand some of the difficulties Holland, with Singstad and three or four other engineers, faced when they met in a bare office the morning they reported for work on what came to be known as the Holland Tunnel. Subaqueous tunneling by means of tunnel shields and compressed air was by no means uncommon at this time, but never on the scale on which they had undertaken to accomplish it. The new tunnel was to accommodate a double line of traffic (a roadbed of twenty feet) in each direction. This would necessitate twin tubes longer than had ever been attempted before and, because of the depth of the Hudson and large size of the tunnel required, these would have to be built under a heavier pressure of water than had ever been attempted. The length of the tunnel complicated the ventilating needs for gas burning vehicles. Because of the scientific facts governing water pressures, the size of the tunnel's diameter complicated pressure problems many times more than the mathematical ratios between various water depths indicate.

The basis of some of the difficulties can be understood if we visualize a little of the process of compressed air and tunnel shield digging. The idea for the tunnel-shield method is borrowed from that of the wood-boring worm which secretes, and exudes as it bores, a lining for the walls of its passage which prevents the walls from caving in behind it. A tunnel shield "bores" forward, driven by a row of hydraulic jacks. Its outer rim cuts and trims the tunnel's circumference. Running back from the cutting edge (and corresponding to the body of the wood-boring worm) is a steel cylinder mechanism which supports a distance of freshly tunneled ground and overlaps the edge of the tunnel wall already in place. The wall is formed of a succession of cast-iron rings, built in segments. At definite stages of progress a new ring is put in place, segment by segment, within the protection of the steel cylinder, and bolted securely to the part of the tunnel wall already in place. Then boring resumes.

Work of this kind done under a heavy body of water has to combat terrific pressure problems. The working chamber must be kept under counter pressure, provided by means of compressed air, sufficient to hold back the rush of dirt and water while digging is going on. A difficult problem in deep subaqueous tunneling is to find how to exert counter pressure which will hold the excavation firm from top to bottom of the shield. This is intensified by diameter size of the shield, because the bigger its diameter the greater becomes the variation in water pressure exerted at the top and at the bottom. Because pressure at the bottom of a sizeable shield is so much greater than at the top, a counter pressure sufficient to hold the bottom firm may blow the river bed out at the top. This problem, on a thirty-foot shield, was intensified tremendously, and had never been met before Holland and his group undertook the Hudson River Tunnel.

Scientific and technological facts had to be determined with the greatest accuracy and skill to determine what size tube would be practical and most economical beneath the Hudson. Equal scientific accuracy was essential in determining how to exert counter pressures which, at varying depths, as the tunnel sloped downward and then back up again, would hold so large a shield firm from top to bottom, assuring safety to workers and success to the project. As chief engineer, Clifford Holland had the responsibility for these problems and most of them were solved before this brilliant young engineer's death. But eventually they were to rest upon Ole Singstad's shoulders.

From the beginning, the ventilating problem was Singstad's. This was so new a problem that existing knowledge was practically nil. The tunnel would have to be more than a mile and a half in length. (When finished, the two tubes averaged 8,463 feet between portals.) All vehicles passing through it would be throwing off exhaust gases, and the capacity would be a minimum of 3,800 vehicles per hour. What would be the amount and composition of their exhaust gases and what would be their effect upon people in the tunnel? These questions had scientific, technological and physiological angles. No one knew the answers.

It was recognized, however, that blowing air through from portal to portal would not be adequate. Shorter horse-and-buggy and pedestrian tunnels had been successfully ventilated in this manner. Long railway tunnels could be ventilated in this way, too, because ventilation was aided by the piston-like action of the trains as they forced currents of air ahead of them. Singstad's design had to permit space for separate pipes and ducts for the ventilating system within the tunnel tubes even though increasing the size of the tubes increased the problems of construction. Eventually the tubes' diameters were set at twenty-nine and a half feet.

The ventilating problem was worked out under Singstad's direction with the cooperation of the U.S. Bureau of Mines. The Bureau's Experiment Station in Pittsburgh investigated the amount and composition of the exhaust gases. The Station at Yale University studied the effects of these gases upon human beings and the necessity for diluting them to render them harmless. The station at the University of Illinois studied the power requirements for ventilating the tunnel. The Bureau of Mines' experimental mine at Bruceton, Pennsylvania, was reconstructed, partially, to provide a miniature tunnel completely shut off from the outside atmosphere except through a passage connecting it to a ventilating plant located outside. Tests were made, and after scientific data were on hand Singstad completed the design. It called for a ventilating system which supplies fresh air at points ten to fifteen feet apart without any high velocity air currents in the roadway area; quickly dilutes and removes exhaust gases into the exhaust duct; is controllable at any one point; and prevents spread of smoke when a fire starts in the tunnel.

Construction of the Holland Tunnel began in 1920. In 1924 Clifford Holland died, and Milton Freeman was appointed to succeed him. Three months later Freeman died. In 1925 Ole Singstad was named chief engineer and superintendent, with the privilege of acting as consulting engineer on other projects so long as such work did not encroach upon time essential to fulfillment of his Holland responsibilities. Late in 1927 the Tunnel was opened, with considerable criticism still being expressed by those who claimed it could not operate effectively. As superintendent, Singstad operated it for two years and a half, and the $48,500,000 pioneer long vehicular tunnel for automotive traffic was a success from the beginning.

Operating on a toll basis, the Tunnel's financial returns were greater than had been immediately expected. Profits over operating costs exceeded $3,500,000 the first year—one half going to each state. More than eight and a half million cars used the Tunnel during its first year's operation. There were no shutdowns except those planned for taking readings on air distribution which would complete scientific data. No serious accidents occurred. Nearly 200 fires broke out in vehicles passing through, and were satisfactorily handled. More than 2,000 disabled cars were towed out of it during the first year alone. Engineers watched with great interest to see if Singstad's ventilating system would be satisfactory under heavy traffic conditions. If it proved successful it would be an impetus to the construction of other long vehicular tunnels. It was a success, and Ole Singstad's status as the world's greatest authority on vehicular tunnels was assured.

Several years before the completion of the Holland Tunnel, Singstad had become a consulting engineer for the George A. Posey Tunnel which connects Oakland and Alameda, California, beneath an arm of San Francisco Bay. The Posey Tube adopted the Holland Tunnel's ventilating system in all its important aspects, as did the next important subaqueous vehicular tunnel to be built, connecting the United States and Canada beneath the Detroit River. In New York Singstad served as consulting engineer for the Lincoln Tunnel, a second vehicular tunnel connecting New Jersey and New York beneath the Hudson, several miles farther north than the Holland Tunnel and duplicating its main features. He also served as consultant on the tunnel approaches to the George Washington Bridge, the most southerly bridge to span the Hudson, completed in 1931.

But a more difficult job than any of these was still ahead —the tunnel connecting Manhattan with Queens beneath the East River. As chief engineer for the New York City Tunnel Authority, Singstad had charge of both its design and construction. Because of the extremely unfavorable ground through which this tunnel had to be cut, and other difficulties which had to be met, this was a job which demonstrated Ole Singstad's capacity for careful and farsighted planning, his ability to coordinate men and operations, and his forcefulness which enabled him to achieve progress and good workmanship in the face of great difficulties.

To begin with, the ground through which the Queens-Midtown Tunnel had to be driven was bedrock in some areas and extremely porous in other areas. Because of the 31-foot tunnel diameter, water pressures were great, necessitating heavy counter pressures through use of compressed air. Because of the porosity of some areas, compressed air escaped in large quantities, often taxing the compressed air plant to its full capacity. The most difficult condition to be met lay in the sections of transition from bedrock to porous ground, where the lower part of the shield faced rock and the upper part porous material. To keep the bed of the river from blowing out over the tunnel it was necessary to lay a thick blanket of clay on the river bed to act as a counter weight. More than four hundred thousand cubic yards of clay were used in this operation, and in one stretch in the channel the tunnel had to be driven through the clay deposit. At that section a layer of broken stone five feet thick was deposited, too, as protection from erosion by the tide.

The gamut of construction difficulties run into while building the Queens-Midtown Tunnel included a fire which broke out from unknown causes in the north tunnel, at a spot where adverse ground conditions had created a major problem. Fire in a compressed air tunnel is intensified by the enormous oxygen content of air under pressure. The fire occurred on a Sunday when the regular gangs of workmen were not on duty and it reached such proportions that it could be put out only by lowering the compressed air pressure in the tunnel and allowing the tunnel to flood with river water. There were no human casualties but it took more than a month to unwater the tunnel, clean up the muck that had flowed into it, and get back to normal tunnel driving operations again.

Despite all difficulties the tunnel was opened for regular traffic ahead of schedule in November 1940, four years and one month after ground had been broken for it. Its cost was $55,000,000, which was several millions less than estimates had called for. On the same pattern as the Holland Tunnel, it had better lighting, larger air ducts, and makes better use of fans than the two earlier tunnels.

Queens Tunnel proved that under efficient engineering and management great tunnels could now be undertaken and completed in a minimum of time. They could be built with a minimum of risk to the health of workmen, too. With the cooperation of the United States Health Service, Singstad made the problem of the health of workers in compressed air a matter of large-scale research on the Queens-Midtown Tunnel project, with gratifying results.

Before the Queens-Midtown Tunnel had been completed Singstad was at work on a still bigger one—the $80,000,-000 tunnel connecting Brooklyn with the tip of Manhattan under New York Harbor. World War II stopped the construction of the tunnel but it was eventually completed in 1950 and is longer than the Holland Tunnel.

Although Singstad withdrew from all but consulting practice in 1945 he has designed, built or been consulted on most of the great underwater tunnels. He is conceded to be one of the world's greatest authorities on vehicular tunnels.

Now at the age of seventy-five he is actively at work on the $66,000,000 Baltimore Harbor Tunnel. This gigantic project promises to be the crowning glory of Singstad's career. Unlike the shield-driven tunnels under New York City this one will be a two-lane tunnel made of prefabricated, double-barreled steel sections laid in a trench dredged in the bottom of the harbor. The sections are bolted together and waterproofed, then cemented into place. Finally sand and gravel are poured in to fill the trench. Singstad was the consulting engineer on such a trench tunnel, the Posey Tube, in Oakland, California, built successfully some thirty years ago. This latest miracle of Singstad's genius is a part of the seventeen-mile Baltimore throughway, which is expected to untie one of the worst traffic tangles in the United States.

During his busy life Mr. Singstad has found time to lecture on subaqueous tunneling, foundation engineering and soil mechanics at the engineering schools at Harvard and New York universities, and to serve on Princeton's advisory council for civil engineering. He has also served on tunnel and highway projects in Belgium, Argentina, Cuba, Venezuela, Canada and Brazil.

Honors have been bestowed upon him by several foreign governments. He is a Decorated Officer of the Order of the Crown of Belgium, a Knight First Class of the Royal Norwegian Order of Saint Olaf, and the honor of membership in the Royal Norwegian Society of Sciences has been conferred upon him.

At home, the American Society of Civil Engineers has honored him with its James Laurie Prize and honorary membership. He holds doctorates from five educational institutions. But it has been New York he has served most fully, and no honor has been more greatly merited than the Abraham Lincoln Award for Distinguished Services on behalf of the City of New York.

Besides serving his professional societies in various capacities he has given time and effort to the Red Cross, the National Research Council, the International Labor Office, and for other civic activities. Still active in his profession, Ole Singstad ranks as one of the most outstanding of the many Norwegian-born, Norwegian-educated Americans who have contributed enduringly to the home they sought in their desire to "see what lies on the other side of the mountains."

John Robert Suman

(1890 –   )

PETROLEUM ENGINEER WHOSE WORK HAS
BEEN GREATLY RESPONSIBLE FOR DOUBLING
THE AMOUNT OF OIL RECOVERED FROM
EARTH'S HIDDEN RESERVOIRS

□□□□□□□□□□□□□□□□□□□□□□□□□□□□

THERE was no such profes-
sion as petroleum engineering when John Suman started out
as an engineer. Nor was there an idea in young Suman's
head that he was aiming at a career in the oil fields. He was
a graduate in mining engineering with considerable interest
in geology and a summer's experience in gold mining. His
first job after college took him to Texas as an assistant
geologist for an oil company. Within a year he was working in the oil fields and he never left them.

True, after Mr. Suman became vice-president and director of the Standard Oil Company (New Jersey) his
headquarters were in the Company's Radio City offices in
New York City and his work took him all over the world.
But the oil fields of the Southwest have really been his
work center, and Texas his home, since he first went there
direct from college. His achievements there in improving
old and developing new petroleum production techniques

have not only vastly increased American oil production; they have had an important part in the development of a new branch of the engineering profession in which young men may now specialize in college and receive their degrees.

Part of the story of John Suman's early life hinges around an educational handicap and what he did about it. Daleville, Indiana, where he was born and grew up, had a population of a few hundred people and a four-room school where the highest grade was the equivalent of an inadequate freshman year in the high schools of that day. John took his education largely as any other happy, well-fed, intelligent youngster takes his early schooling—without much thought about what it is going to mean to him when he grows older. His parents sent him up to Muncie for his second year in high school and there he ran into a little trouble. He found he was not prepared for his sophomore year's work as well as students who had attended the Muncie schools. Then the Sumans moved to California where John had two months in the high school at San Bernardino before the family settled permanently in Los Angeles. He was accepted in the Los Angeles High School in the midst of his junior year's work, graduating the next year.

But four years in four different high schools is never the most satisfactory way of preparing for college and in John's case they had imposed definite handicaps. He had decided, largely as the result of contact with two uncles, prospectors in the Mojave Desert whose specimens of rocks and minerals and talk of mines and lodes and ores had interested him greatly, to study mining engineering. For this he would need mathematical ability of a high order and John had been, at best, but an indifferent student of mathematics. A handicap of more immediate importance was his lack of adequate credits to enter the college of his choice, the Mining College of the University of California.

He solved the immediate problem by taking the general two-year engineering course at the University of Southern California from which he could transfer, if his work was satisfactory, to the Mining College at Berkeley. The other handicap was one which would take genuine effort to overcome and he was extremely fortunate, in his freshman year at "U.S.C." in having Paul Arnold as his mathematics teacher. Without Professor Arnold, Suman admits he might have become one of the hundreds dropped from engineering courses.

"That man really could teach mathematics," he says of Professor Arnold. "First I began to understand it, then I began to get excited about it. Nothing like that had ever happened to me before."

But something had happened to him before his college days which was a constructive experience to bring to his problems now. John Suman had grown up in a home where he had learned to work for what he wanted. In Daleville, his father had been president of the bank, owner of the largest store, of the livery stable and the natural gas wells supplying the community. He believed that growing children should learn the meaning of work and responsibility and his sons had to take job responsibilities early. John's first paid job was to make wooden egg crates and pack the eggs his father's huckster wagons brought back from country trips. Feeding a pig until it was big enough to sell was not a particularly pleasant kind of work but John did that, too, and learned its cash value in boys' shoes and pants.

"Whatever you have in life you will have to earn for yourself," his father told him. "Don't grow up thinking I'm going to accumulate money for you to spend. I'll provide for your education but after that you'll be on your own. When I have enough to educate my family and provide for your mother and me for the rest of our lives, I'm going to retire and spend what I am accumulating."

So when John Suman was ready for college he not only knew he would have to work for what he wanted but he had had considerable experience doing it. He had never known he wanted to be a superior student because that desire had never been awakened in him. Sitting in classes under Professor Arnold he discovered mathematical abilities he never knew he had. Soon he began to discover other intellectual interests. In short, Johnnie Suman was now beginning to find the stuff of which he was made. His intellectual curiosity was so thoroughly aroused that, after he was accepted at the Mining College in Berkeley, he wanted to take more work than the authorities allowed!

One requisite for graduation was a job in a mine, between the junior and senior years, followed by a thesis describing the complete operation of that particular mine, for oral presentation to all mining engineering seniors. Suman's job was as assistant assayer for the Yellow Aster Mining and Milling Company in the Randsburg gold field, at one of the largest gold mines in the country. Some 2,500 tons of ore were mined there every day by the "glory hole" method. Then the ore was pulverized and run over tables coated with mercury. The gold picked up in this way was then retorted and molded into gold bricks—all of which was accurately described in his thesis.

It was a good summer's work with experience which whetted Suman's appetite still further for his last year of college work. During the second semester of that year, sheerly because of interest in everything pertaining to mining engineering and geology, he carried twenty-six hours of academic work. This was considerably more than the topmost limit for which he could register for credits, but the University permitted its better students to sit in regularly on courses beyond those for which credits would be given, and to take examinations if they wanted to.

"I decided to take exams for the whole twenty-six hours

of work," Mr. Suman says. "Exam week arrived, and I found myself in the hospital with mumps! That meant private exams when I was out of quarantine. On top of this, the University authorities belatedly discovered my high school credits were not adequate for granting the State University's degree. They told me if my old high school would cooperate in the matter of granting credits, the University would accept them."

So he took his special examinations, made a hurried trip to Los Angeles where his teachers remembered him and were glad to provide the necessary papers, and went back for graduation. When he received his final marks they were straight "Ones" for the whole twenty-six hours of work. His degree was granted *summa cum laude*, and John Suman's educational handicap was past history.

Like many other mining engineers, he now started out as a geologist. For one hundred dollars a month (and only one man in his class of 1912 did better than that) the Rio Bravo Oil Company of Houston, Texas, a subsidiary of the Southern Pacific Railroad, hired him to assist in a survey of geological formations along the route of the Southern Pacific. His job was to look for mineral deposits of commercial value which, if developed, might increase the freight carried by that railroad. Suman thinks it may have been the resemblance of the oil wells, scattered over the area he was surveying, to the gas wells near Daleville, that attracted him to the oil industry. "I sort of felt at home when I saw them," he says. So, at the end of a year, when he learned that Rio Bravo's chief engineer had been offered promotion elsewhere, Suman applied for the job. Part of his reason for wanting the job was financial, for by this time he had married and had added responsibility. At any rate, a combination of need and desire must have made him persuasive, for the general manager of Rio Bravo decided to take a chance on so young and inexperienced a chief engineer. The Company's operations were not large at that time—a fact which gave Suman a better chance of getting the job.

Since he had so few engineers on his staff, Suman had to be out in the field working at every type of engineering work in the production end of the oil industry. First there was surveying in locating the well sites according to the geologist's blueprints. Then he supervised the riggers who erected the derricks—steel or wooden structures that might be seventy feet high, or twice that height, depending upon the extent of the drilling. Next came the drilling with a rotary rig, then almost exclusively used in the Texas Gulf Coast; and finally the difficult procedure of completing a well and bringing it into production. After the hole had reached the desired depth, long joints of steel pipe or "casing" had to be successively fitted together and lowered into the well. Since gas, oil, and water are frequently encountered in that order in an oil-productive formation, the operations involved in "landing" and cementing the casing at the correct depth are exacting. A serious error will result in excessive gas or water and limited oil production from the well.

Suman learned the practical engineering of oil production as it was carried on in those days, and the more he learned the better he liked the special field of work he had found somewhat by accident. He had a couple of modest raises in salary and his work and personality were winning him good friends in the oil fields. Through one of these friends the offer came, at the end of five years, of the position of technical superintendent of the Roxana Petroleum Corporation's operations in Texas and Louisiana at $350 per month. This was advancement, both in salary and responsibility, and Suman accepted.

Now he ran into the experience of directing, for two years, oil well drilling which cost several million dollars and struck no oil. He had no responsibility, of course, about the failure to strike oil. Geologists decided *where* the wells were to be drilled; and since Roxana was "wild-catting" or drilling in unproven areas, the chances of striking oil were not more than one in ten, at best.

"It was good experience," he says, "and my education was increasing. Still, it became a little discouraging not to be producing oil. When my old company asked me to return to them as assistant to the vice-president and general manager, it was not only the increase in salary and responsibility that was attractive. Rio Bravo was getting oil—and I wanted a job where oil was being produced."

For the next eight years (1919-1927) that is exactly the kind of job John Suman had. He was now not only a top-ranking engineer but an engineer-executive in an industry that was expanding as rapidly as wildfire and, in some ways, it seemed to him, almost as wastefully. The first year after his return to Rio Bravo, some 35,000 wells were drilled in the United States at an estimated cost of $575,000,000 by anybody and everybody who had pro-cured oil rights from land owners and raised the money needed for drilling. If incompetent operators struck gush-ers, millions of barrels of one of our nation's most precious resources were produced wastefully and without any thought being given to the use of engineering principles. Even the best of oil men were getting out of the ground only a fraction of the oil within reach of their successful wells.

As J. B. Davidson had recognized a dozen years earlier in the agricultural engineering field, John Suman now rec-ognized the handicap of the lack of an authoritative refer-ence book for engineers working in the oil fields. Oil had been produced in the United States since 1859 yet few good books had appeared which dealt specifically with problems arising in the drilling of wells, and in the producing and handling of oil. He had already gathered much material out of his own experience, and from the technical journals and from publications of the U.S. Bureau of Mines, which was of great help. When a young engineer came to him with a problem, he could often reach into his desk and show, in print or typewriting, what was already known about the problem. Some people said, "Why don't you put that into a book? It would be useful to a lot of people." Others thought how well it could be used purely for personal advantage. Suman's response was to set himself the task of systematizing available information on what, in his judgment, were best methods in every phase of petroleum production, with the idea of publishing it for everybody's use.

Much of what he selected for publication was his own work. For the rest he secured permission from authors and technical journals to use the articles he needed, with proper credits. The book he prepared, with Mrs. Suman's help in the typing, he called *Petroleum Production Methods*. Publishers refused to print it and Suman had no money to publish it himself. Friends he had made in the oil fields backed him—four of them with five hundred dollars each— and the book was published in 1921. It remained the standard reference book in its field for years, ran through several printings, and more than repaid its backers.

The book also helped make John Suman known as an engineer who, at thirty-one, had learned as much about the techniques and economies of petroleum production as the experience of the industry and his own years of intense study could teach him. Southern Pacific now used him in advisory and managerial positions in some of its other oil subsidiaries. In 1925, it made him vice-president and general manager of the Rio Bravo Oil Company. The efficiency and unusual economy with which this company operated, and Suman's recognized part in it, attracted attention in the industry and brought him opportunities. But not until the Humble Oil and Refining Company of Houston agreed, in 1927, to let him create a petroleum engineering department within its organization did the opportunity come which made him willing to leave Rio Bravo again.

Suman's years with Rio Bravo had been years in which considerable progress had been made throughout the Southwest in the development and application of petroleum engineering techniques. He himself had had two or three engineers working on better methods of drilling and producing oil, but his company was a small one and could not afford large outlays for this kind of work. Some of the larger companies, however, had not only begun to use engineers but were forming petroleum engineering departments. By 1927, a few of these companies actually had well-organized departments and were beginning to do considerable research work. Also, the U.S. Bureau of Mines was carrying on work leading to improvement in production practices.

By this time, too, the industry was awaking to its responsibilities for oil conservation and for disseminating knowledge on petroleum engineering techniques. The American Petroleum Institute had been providing a forum for this purpose and Suman had been taking a prominent part in its activities which resulted, the year he left Rio Bravo, in the publication of the still authoritative *The Function of Gas in the Production of Oil* in cooperation with the Bureau of Mines. As a matter of fact, the Institute's activities were going to consume a great deal of Suman's time for a long period. Though he could not foresee it at the moment, for the next quarter of a century—possibly longer—he would serve on an average of four of its committees every year, frequently as chairman, sometimes on as many as six committees in a year, and for a period on its board of directors.

His early work for the Institute brought rewarding compensations. It gave him association with the top engineers in the country and it was this association which impressed on Suman the great potentialities in research work which could be carried on by an oil company large enough to justify the necessary expenditures. So, as he entered upon his new position with the Humble Company he looked forward not only to the opportunity to select men with specialized knowledge greater than his own (one of Suman's strong points is that he has always been able to recognize how much he does not know), direct them toward petroleum problems, and give them scope and freedom to advance technical knowledge. Because of contacts made through the Institute's work he was also looking forward with confidence to being able to rouse interest in men from other companies who would initiate their own researches.

The problems Suman and others set out to solve in their researches in oil production ranged all the way from how to control the terrific forces in the earth's interior—forces as powerful as those which troubled engineers like Ole Singstad in tunneling beneath a deep river bed—to the less difficult problems concerning the development of the best tools and equipment for oil well drilling and production, together with the standardization of this equipment and its parts. Although the work in standardization alone saved millions of dollars in the oil fields, the control of forces within the earth's crust was the most important of all. If not properly controlled, subsurface pressures, which increase proportionally with depth, would shoot great fountains of oil into the air, and these "gushers," or wild wells, flow in an extremely wasteful manner. Of many times greater significance, however, was the underground loss which so often resulted from failure in subsurface equipment, or from improper production methods. These losses were not easily seen and the improper methods producing them could be recognized only after years of experience and painstaking research.

In the realm of better equipment, Suman played an important part in developing the modern rotary drilling rig from the crude rigs he worked with when he drilled his first wells in Texas. Drilling by the rotary method is achieved by rotation of a drilling bit on the bottom of the hole. The modern rotary drilling rig may be compared to a huge drill press but has the added problems of removing cuttings and lubricating the bit during operation at depths as great as 20,000 feet. Also, provision must be made for replacing a dull bit. In the rig Suman helped develop, the drill stem is made up of sections or "joints" of drill pipe attached to each other by threaded connections. Joints may be added or taken from the drill stem in singles or as many as four at a time ("fourbles"), depending upon the height of the particular derrick in use.

In the modern rig additional heavy surface equipment provides means for simultaneously rotating the hollow drill stem and for pumping drilling fluid down the inside of the drill stem at a high rate and under high pressure. This drilling fluid, more often a special kind of mud, passes through "water courses" in the bit which direct the flow against the cutting edges of the bit and the bottom of the hole. After cooling and lubricating the bit and washing cuttings from the bottom of the hole, pressure forces the drilling mud upward on the outside of the drill pipe, carrying the cuttings with it. Since good drilling mud is difficult to maintain and often quite expensive, it is picked up by the mud pumps and recirculated after the cuttings have been removed.

Suman soon found he needed chemists as well as engineers for his researches in rotary drilling methods. As one significant example, the drilling of certain shales was extremely hazardous due to their sloughing or heaving tendency which sometimes resulted in stuck drill pipe and a junked well. The drilling of other formations resulted in undesirable changes in the drilling mud. A loss in its specific gravity might occur, leading to a loss in weight of the mud column below that necessary to prevent the escape of oil and gas met in the drilling operations. If allowed to continue, this would result in a blowout. So one group of men Suman put on the research job were chemists who sought formulas for the most effective mud!

Interest in better equipment had by no means dulled John Suman to other needs in his industry. Elimination of waste and increased recovery of oil through control of earth's subterranean forces were problems on which he was working, too, as was demonstrated in the fall of 1933, when an emergency arose. In the midst of the development of the Conroe oil field in Montgomery County, Texas, a well belonging to a competing company got out of control. A giant crater was formed into which was lost the derrick, drilling rig, and casing head or "Christmas tree," as this part of the equipment is commonly called. From the crater 9,000 barrels of oil per day were flowing and being collected in pits. All engineers knew that if this unrestricted flow continued the great Conroe field, with reserves of four or five hundred million barrels, would be damaged irreparably and perhaps only half as much oil would be recovered.

Meetings were called by the Texas conservation authorities to develop testimony as to what could be done. Most of the operators thought that nothing could be done, but Suman testified that he thought he could drill a deviated hole from a point on the edge of the great crater to the bottom of the wild well and, by injecting large volumes of water through this relief well, kill the wild well in the crater. This had never been done before but his associates in Humble and some officials of other companies affected had enough confidence in his judgment to pledge around a million dollars to make the try. Suman surrounded himself with his staff and developed a plan for killing the wild well. Without going into details the well was killed within sixty days and a great oil reserve saved. Oil men in Texas talked long about this accomplishment.

The year he killed that wild well was the year Suman became vice-president, in charge of production, of the Humble Company. Probably the most important problem facing him was to learn how to recover more oil from subterranean reservoirs than was then being recovered. As he had learned in his gold-mining experience, Suman knew success in oil operations, too, depended not on the amount in the earth but on the amount brought out retaining commercial value. In early days oil men had accepted that wells might either dry up when only a small percentage of their resources had been recovered, or their oil become so greatly saturated with salt water or gas as to have little or no commercial value. By the early 1930's, better production methods had greatly increased the percentages of recovered oil, and Suman had had a great part in this achievement. He was still thinking about and working on the application of known laws of physics to the problem.

As he visualized our hidden oil reservoirs he knew they were not huge caverns, filled with oil or gas or both, but tiny, connected pore spaces in sandstone and limestone (usually) "reservoir rock." How to tap these reservoirs for greatest eventual recovery was the problem. How close should wells be spaced? How fast should they be allowed to produce? Would such measures as the producing of selected wells, or slower production rates from the reservoir as a whole permit recovery of some oil now considered non-recoverable? Many questions needed answers.

Suman is the last man in the world to allow undue claims about his part in answering these questions successfully. Certainly many men had their part. A few facts speak out, though. The Humble Oil and Refining Company became the biggest oil producer in our Southwest and John Suman had responsibility for its production. The committee of engineers who studied his work before recommending him for the Anthony F. Lucas Medal, presented to him in 1943 by the American Institute of Mining and Metallurgical Engineers for "distinguished achievement in improving the technique and practice of producing petroleum," asserted that research carried on under his direction had revolutionized production methods and established oil-reservoir engineering on a solid foundation resulting in the doubling of recoverable oil. Two years earlier the North Dakota School of Mines had recognized his achievement with an honorary doctorate, and the American Institute of Mining and Metallurgical Engineers had honored him with its presidency.

Indication of the success of recovery techniques worked out in the research laboratories is evident in a few figures for the early 1950's. Recovery of oil contained in the "water drive" type of reservoirs were as high as 80 or 90 per cent, where formerly it ranged from 20 to 40 per cent. In the "gas cap drive" type of reservoirs, recoveries had been raised from 20 per cent to 40 and 50 per cent, and under ideal conditions, to values rivalling those from water drive reservoirs. These techniques were being practiced in many other parts of the world, such as Venezuela and in the Middle East, largely under the direction of American engineers. Certainly the major part of this remarkable accomplishment must be credited to the ingenuity of American petroleum engineers.

In Mr. Suman's estimation, technological achievement

has not been his main contribution to the oil industry or to life. Helping to develop "a wonderful group of younger men," as he puts it, outranks anything else. To him, men rate higher than oil and as he rose to executive and administrative levels he was challenged to find how young engineers could achieve their best development.

"The first thing they needed was a better educational foundation than they were yet able to get," he says, "and after our petroleum engineering department at Humble was instituted I began to be questioned by educators about the best type of curriculum for preparing students for work in the petroleum field. The question had increased importance for oil companies when salaries paid young engineers fresh from college rose from the $100 per month I had received to the $300 per month reached in the 1940's. Economies of production made it essential for us to get commensurate return for such high beginning salaries, and I made myself available to engineering educators to help work out a curriculum for men aiming at the petroleum field.

"Our problems about young engineers at Humble had another aspect, too. People in influential positions with the Company always had friends, or friends of friends, who were about to graduate from engineering schools. We were hiring as many as forty or fifty young engineers some years and there was the constant pressure of 'I'd surely appreciate it if you'd give John—or Bill or Dick—a chance next June.' Obviously Humble was not going to do its duty toward its stockholders, its engineers, or the economical development of our national resources unless we could develop the best possible engineering staff, and John and Bill and Dick were sometimes not the men who had the abilities we needed, or the kind of young men ready to work hard to develop these abilities.

"Finally I had an idea for which I received plenty of thanks later on. We appointed a committee of Humble men to whom full authority for selecting and hiring engineers was delegated. Part of their job was to visit the engineering schools to interview students. When anybody approached one of our executives or directors about giving Bill or Dick a chance in June he was told to tell the young man to get in touch with our representative on his college campus. A formula was worked out by which all applicants were rated and upon which all decisions about hiring men were based. Scholarship had a big but not an overwhelming part in the decision; personality and the opinion of a man's teachers and associates also counted highly. If Bill or Dick made the grade on the basis of this formula, he got a job. If he did not make the grade with that committee, he Did Not Get the Job, Period! It was as definite as that.

"Soon we were able to hire more and more men who had five or six years of college work back of them. The truth is that it is almost impossible to get the training needed for petroleum engineering in four years. Five, and preferably six years, with a master's degree, are better.

"At Humble we put our young engineers at common labor in the field for a year or so, depending upon conditions. This not only gave them actual experience in the jobs over which they would later have some responsibility in our offices, but put them in contact with a group of men of fine character who were wonderful 'character trainers' for young college men. Some of our drillers who could not sign their names to their pay checks were men of character who could teach a young man how to get along with men in the oil field. This whole experience developed self-reliance which was always an asset in later jobs. As a matter of fact, some of our engineers remained in the field by their own preference, though they had originally planned to come into the office.

"Another thing I tried to do was to persuade our young

engineers that unless they genuinely liked doing their work they ought to get out and find work they did like. This holds true, I think, for all young engineers. There's a difference between a young fellow's dream of engineering and its actuality after his degree has been awarded and he is actually performing the work. No man is going to be a success in work he does not like. On the other hand, his chances of success in a work he really does like are great. Life gives a man opportunity to make a second, or even third start, and achieve success. My advice to a young engineer is to face the truth about whether he likes the work he has chosen *after* he is doing it, and if he does not like it, to have the courage to make a second start in something else."

Suman's success with both men and oil was responsible for his call to the Standard Oil Company (New Jersey) in 1945. Wallace Pratt, the friend and neighbor who had persuaded him to leave Rio Bravo for Humble, and had later gone to Standard Oil, was retiring, and the directors asked Suman to take Pratt's place. Possibly nothing short of the biggest oil production job in the world would have tempted John Suman to leave the job he had, but this was it and he accepted. Early in 1945 he became vice-president and director of Standard Oil (New Jersey) and the following January a member of its executive committee.

The new job gave Suman responsibility for oil production in North and South America, Europe, Africa and Asia. Its importance in the post-World War II period can scarcely be overestimated. His efforts were directed not only on getting oil flowing but in developing another "wonderful group of younger men" who are citizens of the countries in which Standard Oil (New Jersey) has holdings. These younger men soon held many of the highest positions in oil production in their own countries. The high capabilities he found in Venezuelan and Egyptian engineers enabled him to turn with confidence to the young men of the Middle East. Although the absence of a middle class in the social system of the Middle East had delayed the development of an educational system capable of preparing students for entrance to engineering colleges, Suman set about developing a group of young men here as he had elsewhere. Standard Oil's policy of not permitting men to work after they reach sixty-five meant that this work had to be put into other hands in 1955.

Retirement for John Suman did not mean an end to his activities and influence in the petroleum industry. It enabled him to become a consultant (with loyalty to the Humble Oil and Refining Company and Standard Oil of New Jersey) with his professional headquarters in Texas which had always remained his home. It also gave him time to renew civic services he had engaged in before his duties had kept him away from home for long periods. Houston remembered him warmly as the man who had once headed its Community Chest Drive, and who had raised funds for the erection of the stadium at Rice Institute. When his retirement was announced the *Houston Post* welcomed him back with the statement that "his return to Houston will bring something back to our town that we lost when he left."

With time off for a trip with Mrs. Suman to Hawaii, New Zealand, Australia and Japan, he settled into the life a man like John Suman enjoys—work for the petroleum industry and for the University of Texas and Rice Institute, work for the cultural life of Houston, contacts with his sons and their families. He golfs and hunts and fishes, finds time for his friends and for the honors that come to him. He is an honorary member of the American Petroleum Institute, and one of his most highly prized possessions is a silver placque presented him for his brilliant leadership in its standardization program.

Carl George Arthur Rosen

(1891 —   )

RESEARCH ENGINEER WHO INVENTED FUEL
INJECTION EQUIPMENT WHICH PUT THE
DIESEL ENGINE ON THE PRODUCTION LINE

⊡⊡⊡⊡⊡⊡⊡⊡⊡⊡⊡⊡⊡⊡⊡⊡⊡⊡⊡⊡⊡⊡⊡⊡⊡⊡

T HE young man who wants
to succeed in engineering has to be able to understand
mathematics. He must be able to comprehend, not merely
memorize, the principles of the sciences basic to engineering. If he wants to specialize in engineering research
Arthur Rosen believes that a zest for adventure is one of
the best personal qualifications he can add to his capacity
for understanding the fundamentals of mathematics, physics, and chemistry.

Mr. Rosen's opinion is based on over a quarter of a
century's experience in engineering research during which
he has watched, helped direct, directed and worked with
hundreds of young men in this field. It is his belief that
engineering research offers exciting possibilities for the
young man who dares to wander into unknown paths, provided he has acquired the fundamental training and the
discipline of mind which enables him to control daring with
sound knowledge and personal intelligence.

Arthur Rosen's parents gave good evidence that they had in their genes whatever it takes for "daring to wander into unknown paths." Each had pulled up stakes in Sweden, had come to America, and gone on to California. A year later they were married in San Francisco where the young husband found work as the master mechanic on the Union Street cable railway. One year later a son was born and christened Carl George Arthur. When Arthur was a year old and beginning to make his wants known by his first few words in Swedish, the family moved across the Golden Gate Strait to Sausalito where Arthur's father went into business for himself as a carriage and wagon maker. A blacksmith shop was part of such an establishment in the 1890's and Arthur, as a small boy, watched his father forge iron parts at his anvil and perform all the other work that went into the construction of vehicles for what was called the "fancy carriage trade." Sausalito was a prosperous and fashionable community in which the carriage drawn by a spanking pair of bays was supposed to measure up in every way to the horses harnessed to it. A durable, smart-looking carriage was something a skilled craftsman might fashion with his own hands, and take pride in.

What could have been more natural, then, than that small Arthur Rosen began early to fashion with his own hands the things he wanted? Pieces of wood, metal of various shapes and sizes were to be found in his father's shop. They offered fascinating possibilities to an eager child whose initiative seems to have matched his father's. Here was a boy who loved tools, and who lived in the day before mass production and five- and ten-cent store standards destroyed part of a youngster's initiative by making many things available cheaply that an earlier generation had to make for themselves or do without. Looking about the shop where his father gave him considerable freedom, Arthur's mind pondered over how he could make tools and toys for himself, and his hands almost automatically set to work on them. One of his earliest-remembered achievements was a hacksaw made, when he was eight or nine, out of a wagon wheel and a narrow strip of saw.

In those years which history dubs the Gay Nineties, the Gold Rush to Alaska was making an impression upon some of the small boys in Arthur's community. Sausalito's harbor was a sheltered spot where sailing ships constantly dropped anchor on their way to or from the Klondike and Yukon regions of the Northwest. Every California youngster knew there was gold in California, too, and Arthur Rosen used to organize groups of small boys into expeditions which searched for gold in the hills about Sausalito. These always unsuccessful expeditions lost some of their lure when the boats in the harbor finally registered in Arthur's mind that comparatively small sailing vessels could make their way to Alaska where gold was plentiful. The boy who had so often created the equipment to serve his needs now set to work to solve a new problem confronting him—how to get the gold everybody was talking about. With two companions of similar age—nine years—and without mentioning it to parents, they took over an open, round-bottom sailboat belonging to Arthur's father. In it they stored hardtack and a few other supplies including an old compass, and set sail for Alaska.

The completely unseaworthy boat was washed ashore, right side up, long before it could pass through the Gate into the Pacific. The boys returned home; and one, at least, had learned something about round-bottom boats.

Arthur was now nine and his father's business had prospered well enough for him to purchase a wagon-making establishment in San Francisco and move his family back to that city. The Swedish shipsmith immigrant of a dozen years earlier was now the proprietor of one of the fair-sized wagon-making establishments on the West Coast. Arthur transferred to San Francisco schools and by the time he came out of grammar school (and without ever making a conscious decision about it) he knew he wanted to become an engineer. Instead of sending him to high school his parents now sent him for four years to the Cogswell Polytechnical College. Cogswell was the best preparation possible for the engineering school at the University of California. In addition to its high-school course, accredited by the University, it put special emphasis on the industrial arts and sciences. But it was the teaching at Cogswell which was its greatest advantage. Classes often numbered no more than ten or twelve, seldom more than twenty.

"I had teachers who were engineers," Mr. Rosen says, "men like George Miller who taught me mathematics with an engineer's background and approach and helped me understand mathematics as a live tool to be applied to the solution of problems. Another man to whom I owe a lot was Professor Burkhart who taught engineering mechanics and design. Men like these, in classes conducted more like seminars than on the mass educational techniques prevalent in many high schools, enabled me to learn how to study and how to think. They were grounding me early in the fundamental techniques of engineering."

These teachers seem also to have developed in Arthur Rosen a lifelong desire to teach. Although he was headed for engineering research in industry, he never removed himself completely from opportunity to teach younger engineers. His early engineering education impressed upon him, too, the belief that many of the young men who have given up engineering studies because of difficulty with mathematics could have understood mathematics with better teaching.

"Almost anybody can understand mathematics," Rosen says and earnestly believes. "Understanding should come before college days. It should begin before high school days. But the young fellow who has difficulty with high school 'math' should not let himself become too much discouraged. If he works and can find the right help from teachers, the door of his mind will open. I feel my personal experiences both in learning and in teaching give me authority to state this as a fact."

Because of the fundamental training in engineering at Cogswell, Rosen had greater latitude at the University of California in the selection of courses in the liberal arts. He took considerable work in English literature. In his engineering work there, one event turned out to be of the greatest importance to his whole future. A Scotsman (his name was Scott) lectured at the University on the Diesel engine and from that time on Rosen's interest centered on the Diesel engine. He knew so definitely the field of his special interest that when he received his B.S. in Mechanical Engineering in 1914 and could not find work in the Diesel field, he did not allow himself to be taken away from his special interest.

To understand his situation at that time, a little background of Diesel engine history is necessary. The engine's inventor was a German, Rudolph Diesel. His engine differed from other internal combustion engines in that in the usual internal combustion engine (i.e., the gasoline engine) air and fuel are mixed *before* they enter the cylinder for compression, while in the Diesel engine oil is injected into the cylinder to meet the air *after* the air is compressed. Efficient power, and important fuel economies were possible with Diesel's invention—facts of the utmost importance in the engineering and economic world. Diesel himself had visited the United States while Rosen was in college, and had read a paper before the American Society of Mechanical Engineers in which he asserted that his engine doubled the resources of mankind in regard to power production. And the engine was only in the infancy of its development.

Diesel, of course, held patents on his engine. It could be manufactured only with his license. When Arthur Rosen came out of college only five firms in the United States held such licenses. Two of them were in St. Louis, one in Auburn, New York. The fourth license was held by a firm in Connecticut and the fifth by a company in Alameda, California, a small company interested in Diesel engines for stationary power plants and for marine use in ships and on small work boats. Unfortunately it had no opening for young Rosen when he graduated from college. So Rosen accepted a fifteen-dollar-a-week job as draftsman in a near-by office while he thought things over and waited to see if the picture at the Dow plant might change.

It soon became evident that the job he had taken was going to do nothing for him at all. Yet there was still no opportunity at the Dow plant and this was his only possibility for Diesel work on the whole Pacific Coast. Looking around him with his eyes wide open, Rosen saw in the Panama Pacific Exhibition, scheduled for San Francisco in 1915, an opportunity that might serve him temporarily. Like his father before him, he set up in business for himself. Capitalizing on his manual skill and engineering education he made miniature power plant models for the Exposition. With pleasant persistency he kept going in to see the chief engineer of the Dow Company and he did not go empty-handed, merely to ask for a job. He kept reading everything he could find about Diesel engines, especially in the German publications the Dow engineer could not read, and usually had some interesting new information to pass along. His persistency bore fruit within a year. Rosen was given a job as draftsman for the Dow Company.

So it was more the result of geography than of decision that Arthur Rosen's early work in the Diesel engine field was on marine engines rather than on the railway Diesels, development of which started farther east some years later. The original Diesels had been stationary engines, and engineers in 1915 were working to adapt the Diesel principle for engines to be used for power generation and ships. Rosen's outstanding achievement while with the Dow Company was his successful adaptation of a stationary Diesel of British design as a marine engine for a moving vessel. Several unique features of his adaptation were forerunners of later American practice. In the course of his work he rose to become chief engineer of the Diesel section for his company and was released by them for a period during World War I to help the United States Navy Trial Board solve certain problems arising in the Navy destroyer program.

As he worked actively in the Diesel engine field Rosen's head was filled with ideas for smaller Diesels that might be used profitably in various industries. All such ideas needed research—more extensive and expensive research than a small company like his own could undertake. For this reason, when the Dow executives changed policy to give attention to oil pumps for the rapidly expanding petroleum industry, Rosen left the company to establish his own consulting engineering business. As a specialist on Diesel problems he knew he could find plenty of consulting work around San Francisco. In business for himself, he could take time to develop some of his ideas on the Diesel to the point of showing commercial possibilities, and time to make contact with firms who might be interested in developing his ideas commercially.

For six years he kept hammering away on this line of attack. As a consultant he was called upon for practically all the Diesel problems of vessel owners in the San Francisco district, and by the United States Shipping Board as well. Also, for five of these years he was able to satisfy his urge to teach by serving as instructor in Diesel engines for the University of California Extension Course.

"I loved teaching," he says. "I still love it and think there is nothing more important than helping young engineers clarify their thinking, which is what good teaching ought to do." The teaching seemed of more importance to him than did the M.E. degree he had earned by the end of his five years.

With it all he was pegging away on ideas aimed at broadening the uses to which the Diesel might be put, and looking for industrial organizations that might give him opportunity to bring some of his ideas to reality. To interest industrialists in the feasibility of smaller Diesel engines, however, proved to be a hard task. Diesels at that time weighed as much as 250 pounds for each horsepower developed. Though they gave economies in performance, heavy engines were too expensive to build for many uses, and too massive, still, for all but a comparatively few purposes. It was 1934 before the first three-car, Diesel-powered, streamlined train was ready for its initial run. So it will be seen how early Rosen's work was when, seven years before this first spectacular run, he persuaded the Caterpillar Tractor Company to let him undertake, at their San Leandro plant near San Francisco, the work which he thought would prove, as it actually did prove within a year, the feasibility of the Diesel as a prime mover for tractors.

In 1928, therefore, Caterpillar launched the program which successfully pioneered the tractor Diesel engine. The program centered at its San Leandro plant, with Arthur Rosen as engineer in charge. Rosen's job was to develop the engine to practical working form for production at the Peoria, Illinois, plant. But this had to be preceded by more extensive research than he had yet made. He reviewed and reported on 250 patents, on Diesel literature in several languages, and on forty-eight commercial engines already in use. No one of these engines was suitable for the tractor. The first full Diesel tractor engine was then designed and constructed under his supervision, in 1930, and an improved engine put into production within two years. It came quickly into demand as replacement for gasoline engines in tractors.

"Maybe the layman can understand some of our tasks better," Mr. Rosen suggests, "if he realizes something about our business in 1930. At that time an engine or tractor might be withdrawn from one of our warehouses for use by native labor in swamps in an African jungle. Or it might be harnessed to a snowplow in the North for use in sub-zero weather; or it might have to travel through clouds of dust over pulverized fields under the control of a be-goggled, closely masked operator; or drag logs through woods over rough country, sometimes up grades as steep as seventy-five per cent. In many of these sections of the world it might be forced to consume a variety of low-grade fuels."

One great advantage of Diesel-engined tractors was their capacity to use cheaper, and a greater variety of, fuels. This made them saleable in corners of the world where high grade gasoline was lacking, or too expensive for trac-tor use. The system by which these cheaper fuels were injected into the cylinder was one of the important fea-tures of Diesel success, and the German system used in the first Caterpillar engines soon offered difficulties. Rosen him-self, while still in California, had invented a balanced-type, constant-pressure fuel valve and regulating mechanism, and he now instituted the researches which eventu-ated in a highly satisfactory Caterpillar fuel injection system. The engine gave good service. The popularity of the Diesel-powered tractor grew. Sales mounted steadily. Then disaster struck!

Caterpillar Diesels began to fail as early as 300 hours. Ring sticking in the cylinders, and ring and cylinder scratching were apparent. Neither the cause nor the remedy were known. Responsibility fell heavily on Arthur Rosen's shoulders.

Researches soon convinced him that the cause of the trouble lay in the lubricating oil. A new method of refining oils had been instituted at the refineries which enabled them to use certain crude oils more successfully than had hitherto been possible. Oils refined by the new solvent method actually gave a cleaner operating performance, but their use unquestionably resulted in ring sticking in Diesels. Rosen made his reports and the refiners placed blame on the engine. Rosen instituted a program to improve the engine mechanically but the problem proved difficult and sales were already falling off alarmingly.

Mr. Rosen became convinced (through research, at which he was truly expert) that the solution lay not alone in engine improvement but in an effective additive in the lubricating oils. The men at the refineries were not easy to convince, but Arthur Rosen had capacity for cooperation and, eventually, he had proof of the effects of a proper additive. Conferences with oil company officials resulted in plans for the men at the refineries to put a new cleaning additive in their oils. Caterpillar and the refineries entered upon joint research activities. Mr. Rosen earned recognition as an expert in lubrication problems. Largely through his efforts standard tests for approving lubricating oils for Diesel engines were based more upon performance in engines rather than on laboratory analyses and bench tests. These standard tests were of great value to our Army and Navy during World War II.

By the latter 1930's success of its tractors had greatly expanded Caterpillar business. Diesels were everywhere at work—in harvest fields where they had minimized fire hazards, on road construction where bulldozers were performing new miracles of earth moving. Mr. Rosen's researches continued; his technical papers were awaited with interest wherever engineers worked on Diesel problems. Then World War II came, to change the face of industry. Production problems alone, in a plant of Caterpillar's potentialities, put heavy responsibility upon everyone. And again, as had been true when its Diesel engine had failed, "Art" Rosen's capacity for cooperation with experts in other industries was going to become of great importance —this time to our whole war effort. It happened like this:

The U.S. Navy had instituted its program to build Diesel engines—engines whose total capacity would reach fifty million horsepower. If these engines were not to be hampered in effectiveness, all existing knowledge on torsional vibration needed to be put in the hands of every company participating in the Navy's engine-building program. This knowledge was scattered among the research departments of industries all over the country, including Caterpillar's research department, and usually held secret. Now, neither Caterpillar nor any other company could do the best job for the Navy unless this knowledge were made available.

Stimulated by Captain Lisle F. Small of the Navy, the Society of Automotive Engineers appointed a small committee, with Rosen as chairman, whose job was to pool, organize, and make available for engine builders participating in the Navy program, all existent knowledge on torsional vibration. Mr. Rosen approached his part of the Committee's work with deep personal conviction that the knowledge should be freely given. He was one of the big reasons why the job was so successfully completed.

A more spectacular job of the war period was his service on the U.S. Naval Technical Mission in Europe. The Mission's job was to follow Allied invading Armies closely, and salvage German research and development projects before they could be destroyed. Rosen was largely responsible for locating scattered parts of the new submarine the Germans had perfected in the few months before their collapse. Four thousand miles of jeep driving finally uncovered all the parts—some found in salt mines a thousand feet underground, some in manure piles in Austria, others submerged under water, and so on. The pieces were sent to the United States, reassembled and evaluated. This submarine, which could remain under water and in operation for over 10,000 miles without surfacing, was one of the reasons why our technical men felt that if the German technical program had been advanced only three months, the war might have been prolonged for three more years.

Soon after our entry into the war, Mr. Rosen had become director of research for the Caterpillar organization. Caterpillar had no independent research department prior to its Diesel engine-research and-development program, when it had been instituted with a personnel of twenty men. During Rosen's regime as its director its staff had grown to more than five hundred and fifty. Other employees had increased less than fourfold in that period while the research department staff had increased twenty-eight fold. The figures indicate the value this company grew to place upon research. Health conditions eventually made it advisable for Mr. Rosen to relinquish his administrative duties and act in an advisory capacity until his retirement in 1957 while continuing his own research work.

Mr. Rosen has a philosophy about his work which has grown with the years. He believes that soundness in technological research is based upon the same fundamentals which make for soundness elsewhere in a man's life. The research engineer's job is to uncover information about the operation of the laws governing the universe which is still unknown. Rosen's conviction is that all laws operating in the universe are based within one abiding Universal Law, and that to understand one fundamental principle—the principle beneath mathematics, for example—is to achieve contact with the root source of all principles. To him, Universal Law is the operation of a Creative Mind which rules the universe, and man has the capacity to become attuned to the Creative Mind, in his work life as in other realms of life.

In engineering research, a man's job, he says, is to advance knowledge in some corner of the whole technological field by finding out certain things which already exist in the Creative Mind.

"A research man never achieves something *new*," he insists. "He reveals what already exists in Creative Mind."

How, then, can a man best learn to reveal what already exists in the Creative Mind? This is the "sixty-four dollar question" which Rosen cannot answer fully. But he answers it in part when he says: by (1) the spirit of adventure added to (2) mental discipline and (3) the will to serve. A spirit of adventure means a man has faith in a vision of some kind. Mental discipline and a will to serve are what give a research man's faith a chance to become visible reality.

Mr. Rosen's awakening to the place of faith in a man's life began as a child when his mother said so often, "There is a Rock that is higher than I." With a child's capacity for understanding, something of the truth of this statement took hold of him. His faith began to waver during college days when he was doing more and more thinking for himself, in an environment when it was fashionable to call faith in the Rock old-fashioned and superstitious, with no basis in fact. Many scientists in those days who tried to explode what they called the God-myth taught students that the atom was the smallest subdivision in Nature and would never be exploded. Exposed to such attitudes, Rosen wavered. But as he began to achieve greater maturity of mind, his conception of a Rock higher than himself began to grow to maturity, too. He no longer thought of it in childish mental pictures. He began to recognize a Something higher than himself as Creative Mind governing the Universe, and that he might come closer to it through faith and work.

At one period of his life he discovered that his moments of waking each morning were giving him his clearest glimpses into this Creative Mind. Many young people have experienced this moment-of-waking flash of understanding that solves a problem hours of mental effort the night before had failed to solve. Rosen had experiences of this kind and found he could foster them by a brief period of meditation each morning as he was waking. For many people these are the moments of greatest clarity on any problem —whether the problem is one of work, or of other aspects of living. For Arthur Rosen these moments have been greatly rewarding.

The will to serve which has been beneath Mr. Rosen's technological achievements has been exercised, too, in his life as a citizen of the communities in which he has lived. Peoria's "Exhibition Gardens," a community center with educational and recreational facilities came into being largely because of Mr. Rosen's vision and work as head of its Planning and Construction Committee. Here, again, his capacity to secure cooperation has been a great factor in the project's success. A spectacular feature of his ability to secure cooperation came when thirty-three different concerns brought two million dollars' worth of earth-moving equipment to a site where earth had to be removed for this civic project, and moved 240,000 cubic yards of dirt in forty and one half hours of continuous performance.

Earth moving is a type of work in which Mr. Rosen has historic as well as present-day interest. Among his many papers are some describing the work of engineers in earth moving and road building, from pre-Christian days down to the present. On trips to South America and Europe he has inspected thousands of miles of ancient and modern roadways from the air, and experienced the satisfaction of knowing how much human back-breaking effort has been removed from road building through Diesel engine-powered machinery. Among his published technical papers the most comprehensive is, *Significant Contributions of the Diesel Engine Laboratory*, which was delivered originally as the James Clayton Lecture, by honored invitation of the British Institution of Mechanical Engineers. He has been a frequent lecturer not only in America and England but before scientific and other groups in Western Europe where he has traveled widely, and in Hawaii. His achievements in engineering and his thinking and observations beyond the technical aspects of his profession have provided him with a background that makes his lectures appeal not only to engineers and scientists but to people whose interests lie outside the fields of science and technology.

In 1950 Mr. Rosen was selected as one of the five most outstanding graduates of the School of Engineering of the University of California, by its alumni group. Twice he has received honorary doctorates from other universities. In 1955 he had the honor of serving as the fiftieth president of the Society of Automotive Engineers.

After his retirement from the Caterpillar Tractor Company Mr. Rosen returned to California where he is on the staff of the mechanical engineering department of Stanford University. He reserves some of his time for private consulting work and still other time for the lecturing that is constantly requested of him.

Stanwood Willston Sparrow

(1888–1952)

AUTOMOTIVE ENGINEER WHO HAS CON-
TRIBUTED TO BETTER AIRPLANES IN TIME
OF WAR AND BETTER AUTOMOBILES IN TIME
OF PEACE

◫◫◫◫◫◫◫◫◫◫◫◫◫◫◫◫◫◫◫◫◫◫◫◫◫◫◫◫◫

O NCE he had discovered his special engineering interest, opportunity for continued research and experimental work on internal combustion engines was what "Stan" Sparrow always wanted out of a job. Promotions came to him—the type of promotion, finally, which meant administrative duties that lessened the time he could devote to his own experimental work. In 1945 he became vice-president of the Studebaker Corporation, in charge of its engineering. But few men have reached high-level jobs in American industry who have been less eager for promotion than Stanwood Sparrow.

Mr. Sparrow is a modern version of those New England mechanics who gave the term "Yankee ingenuity" a high place in America's industrial history. With a twentieth century engineering education and background he kept solving problems besetting gasoline engines, with native knack and an extraordinary insight into how and when an increasing fund of information on enough little problems can add up to a better engine. He has been described by contemporaries as a man with the faculty of seeing through and all around a problem with a clarity that seems to be automatic. He has been compared with a halfback, carrying the ball, who has an uncanny sense about how to weave in and out of whatever stands in his way as he drives toward the goal he has in mind. When Sparrow reached a goal he said, "Well, there wasn't much to that," and started out for a higher score.

As a growing boy the machinery in the engine room of the textile mill where his father worked as a millwright always had special attraction for him. In fact, he found some excuse for being in this room in the mill at the foot of the hill every day for years. Middleborough, Massachusetts, where he lived with his parents and an older sister, was an industrial community, and its industries were small enough to permit a millwright's son to be in and out of his father's workplace, provided he was the type of boy who did not make a nuisance or a risk out of his presence there. Stan had opportunity to absorb what he could from intimacy with his father's work. It dulled, a little, the disappointment of not being able, upon graduation from high school, to accept a scholarship which would have paid his tuition for his freshman year in college. (The scholarship would have taken him to a college where he would not have found courses in mechanical engineering.)

The reason Stan could not accept the scholarship was that his parents could not supply him, that year, with the money he would have needed in addition to the funds from the scholarship. The Sparrows were a New England family who respected higher education. Children were sup-

posed to go to college even though it meant sacrifice, and
Stan's older sister had gone to normal school and prepared
herself for teaching. But wages for factory employees in
Stan's youth were not high, and small emergencies—illness
or layoffs—could wreck a family savings account. College
expenses in 1906, low though they seem in comparison with
such expenses in later decades, were high for families in a
New England factory town. Mrs. Sparrow was handy
with a needle, and she turned her gift to good account in
helping add to the family income. Even so, it was going
to be necessary for Stan to help himself before he could
go to college. And if he was going to earn money of his
own before he went, he could have the satisfaction of going
to a college where he could study what he wanted most.

The first job he got after high school graduation would
not have taken him to college very quickly. One of Middleborough's industries was a planing and molding mill, and
it was here Stan first found work. For six dollars a week he
sandpapered and rubbed pieces of wood to be used in finishing the interiors of homes, and swept up the sawdust and
shavings that littered the floor of the mill. He was a combination janitor and helper, working from seven in the
morning until five in the afternoon six days a week. If he
saved every cent of his wages, in a calendar month he could
save about twenty-six dollars. At that rate college was a
long way off.

Another Middleborough industry was a shoe factory
where jobs were paid for at piece-rate wages. Before too
many six-dollar weeks had passed Stan was at work in the
shoe factory earning around thirty-five dollars per week.
To earn it he stood at a work bench for more than fifty
hours each week, performing the motions of two or three
operations over and over again. Approximately, this is what
he did: He walked to a section of the room where shoes
were delivered on racks, selected a rack, wheeled it to his

work bench, picked up each shoe and with two tacks attached a leather shank of proper size. Next he picked up a putty knife and with it spread a sticky mixture of ground cork over the space between the shank and the welt. This process was repeated for all the shoes on the rack and then he was ready to tackle a new rack.

He liked that job and looks back upon it as a good and a happy experience. Nor was his liking due merely to the fact that he was able to earn good money for his seventeen years. A friendly rivalry existed between workers which gave a certain zest to each day's work. Stan enjoyed doing individual work in a team of workers as he enjoyed doing his individual work on a team of hockey players. The men he worked with had equal opportunity for equal pay and all but two of them actually earned, week after week, approximately the same amount. One of the two exceptions, by straining every moment of the day, and the other by being extremely methodical, earned a couple of dollars more each week than their fellows. No one held it against them and no one chose to emulate them.

Actually, the men made a game out of their work and enjoyed it. One rack might have eighteen pairs of shoes while another might have ten. It was a case of first come, first served, and the one who handled the most shoes had the most money to handle at the end of the week. There was opportunity, there was independence. Effort was rewarded, and there was satisfaction in a rivalry based on a cooperative as well as a competitive spirit.

Sparrow liked the kind of relationships he had with his fellow workers on that job and he never got over liking friendly relationships with the many men with whom he worked. He never hankered to be a lone-wolf type of worker. Earlier, as a schoolboy, he had earned a bicycle through door-to-door selling and realized he would never be happy in business if business entailed individual salesmanship. At eighteen, after his first year's experience in industry, he found his "tack and spread" shoe shank job had left him with a pleasurable feeling for industry.

That next fall he entered Worcester Polytechnic Institute to study mechanical engineering. He described the work there as ". . . pretty rugged. It required practically fulltime work for me and left very little time for extra-curricular activities." Freehand drawing was the subject he disliked most and mathematics the subject he learned with least effort, probably, "though I had no particular fondness for it. Vacations were what I liked most about my college life. I had summer jobs which did not require any strenuous effort. The college work that always pre-ceded these jobs made me appreciate a few months of work that did not take too much effort."

One thing he enjoyed about his life in Worcester was its theaters. Stan's college days were in the heyday of vaude-ville which he enjoyed, and Worcester was on the New England circuit where plays for the legitimate stage often tried out, preliminary to their opening in New York, or toured after their season on Broadway. The theater re-mained a lifelong interest with him. Another thing he found time for in college days was to help in preliminary plans for a new publication called the *Tech News*. Al-though he never served on the staff of this paper he was becoming aware of the importance of being able to write. Early in his post-college days he began to contribute to the technical press and his papers always exhibited the complete clarity that comes not only from a writer's know-ing what he wants to say, but from the personal effort that accompanies clarity in writing. His technical papers often have a dry wit which brings a smile when the reader, or audience, is least expecting it.

With his graduation in 1911 came an opening with a New England tool company for the following September.

"I decided I'd take a vacation that summer," Mr. Sparrow said, "because I figured that would be the last vacation I'd have in a good, long time. So I was enjoying being lazy when, along in August, came a letter from a friend saying he had heard the firm with whom I thought I had a job would not be taking on any new men at the end of the summer. I wrote immediately, and discovered I had been fired before I even went to work."

His next job folded up under him, too, though not with such speed. Over in Chicopee Falls the Stevens Duryea Company had its automobile manufacturing establishment. Nineteen years earlier the Duryea brothers had built the first successfully operated American gasoline engine "horse-less buggy" and several years later won the first motor vehicle contest in America. That contest (to win it, the Duryea buggy covered a muddy course of about fifty-five miles in seven and a half hours despite stops and accidents necessitating sixteen miles of extra travel) had established the superiority of gasoline power over steam or electricity for automobiles, and gasoline engines had made great strides since then. So the Duryea factory was a good place for a young engineer, when Stan Sparrow found an opening there.

After a month's work in its repair shop, he was put into the drafting room for a year. Then a place was found for him in the experimental department. Here Sparrow really began to recognize his engineering interest. But after two years the Stevens Duryea Company went out of existence and Sparrow found himself over in Waltham as assistant chief draftsman for the Metz Company. There was one advantage the Metz job offered a young engineer on a draftsman's job. Because it was a small concern, he had close contact with the designs of all the company's engineers and, as Sparrow put them in shape, he learned about a greater variety of engineering work than he would have been likely to learn in a larger organization.

While he enjoyed his work at Metz, his financial future did not appear too promising. After three years he found a better paying job with the Robert T. Pollock Company in Boston. It was design work, with more money, but it looked as though he had bid farewell to engines and that bothered him. It did not bother him long, however, for soon the Pollock Company was engaged in the design of jigs and fixtures for the Liberty airplane engine and he was back in the groove he liked.

He was now nearly thirty years old, had had seven years of engineering experience, and knew something about jobs which did, and which did not interest him. In 1918 an opportunity came which seemed to be just what his heart desired. He went to the Bureau of Standards to work on tests being made there on the Liberty and Hispano-Suiza engines. From that moment on Stan Sparrow never knew what it was to have a restless desire to leave any job he was on for another one—not even when the vacancy occurred which gave him the Studebaker vice-presidency.

The engine tests to which he was assigned when he reported for work in Washington took place in an altitude chamber which had been constructed in the dynamometer laboratory of the Bureau of Standards. In it, airplane engines and other apparatus could be tested, on the ground, under conditions approximating those met in flight. It was the first of its kind, and had been devised because airplanes were incapable of carrying sufficient apparatus to measure engine performance in actual flight. In the altitude chamber, air pressure and temperature variations, such as an airplane engine had to meet at various altitudes, could be induced at will. Sparrow's job was to operate engines under the various conditions, and find facts. Sometimes the facts concerned engine design, sometimes they concerned the characteristics of fuels or carburetors or spark plugs.

Real facts about anything connected with aviation were scarce in those days and it is difficult to evaluate how much the aviation industry owes to the facts which came from the research in the altitude laboratory of the Bureau of Standards.

In this type of work Stan Sparrow found himself. His interest was gripped not only by what the tests revealed but by the possible *whys* beneath the facts. Soon he was contributing to the growing knowledge about the whats and whys of internal combustion engine problems. One of his technical papers published during this period, "Flying an Airplane Engine on the Ground," gives a rather clear picture of the type of work that was carried on in the Altitude Laboratory during those early days.

There was nothing spectacular in what Sparrow was accomplishing. His field was not one in which some one brilliant engineer contributes some one outstanding discovery which revolutionizes engine design. It was one in which many men contribute the mass of data on which solid progress can steadily be built. Sparrow was forging ahead as one of these men whose aim has been to create better and better gasoline engines as the foundation upon which safe, speedy and efficient, rather than spectacular transportation—whether by automobile or airplane—could be achieved. Diesel engines, eventually jet propulsion, would arrive to serve some purposes better than gasoline engines. But the gasoline engine would have its important place for a long time to come.

With the end of World War I our National Advisory Committee on Aeronautics instituted many types of researches at the Bureau of Standards, and Sparrow was soon at work on these. In 1922, stimulated by the possibility of eventual serious oil shortages which World War I had revealed, the Bureau undertook, also, a fuel research program sponsored by the Society of Automotive Engineers, the

American Petroleum Institute, and the National Automobile Chamber of Commerce. Here was more work for Sparrow, and in the course of it his position rose to chief of the Bureau's power plant section, in which his work was centered. But what he did in those years was far more varied than the titles of his ascending jobs. For example: What caused preignition? What fuel blends were best for high compression engines? What were the relative merits of large slow-speed and small high-speed engines? What relationship to engine performance did the fuel-air ratio have? What did temperatures at the time of intake have to do with engine performance? These questions indicate a few of the problems to which his researches and tests added knowledge. He tested benzol and ethyl alcohol in high compression airplane engines, searching for greater power through fuels with less tendency to detonate than gasoline. In 1925 he published, with J. O. Eisinger, a paper describing "Recent Cooperative Fuel-Research Progress."

Sparrow was happy in his work at the Bureau as a man can be happy when he gets up every morning looking forward to a day working at what interests him most. He was neither looking for nor anticipating another job when W. S. James, once his chief at the Bureau but then head of the Studebaker Corporation's research department, asked him to take charge of engine-development work at South Bend. James knew Sparrow as a man, as a fellow worker and as an engineer. He wanted him at Studebaker, and in time Sparrow said "Yes" and left the Bureau of Standards in 1922.

Although some of his work on the new job might be similar to the research work at the Bureau, another dimension would now always be present. That dimension was immediate and constant competition of the engine he worked on with those of other companies. As head of the engine-development section of his company's research department, Sparrow's immediate job was to take a Studebaker engine which had been built over designs intended to meet predetermined requirements, put it through endurance tests on a dynamometer, measure it for fuel and oil consumption and other performance essentials, and determine as far as possible *before it was put in a car* if it would accomplish what the company wanted and expected it to accomplish. Automobile manufacturers had to meet many problems of appearance, of comfort, and performance, because of competition with other manufacturers. No problem, probably, was quite as important to the majority of car operators and owners, and hence to manufacturers, as "What will the engine do? How will it perform on clear highways and on crowded street corners? What will it do in emergencies, and how long will it keep running with a minimum of attention?"

Here was a job impossible to solve once and be done with it. It had to be solved and re-solved as science and technology brought changes and improvements in all the fields related to automobile construction. Here was a job where, carrying the facts as they existed at the moment, the engineer must weave in and out of technical blocks and opportunities as a halfback weaves his way to the goal. The way was not merely through and around some competitor's team. Did some new metal offer the opportunity of a better piston or connecting rod? Use that opportunity! New processes at oil refineries brought new problems in fuel and lubrication. Weave a way around those problems! New designs altered wind resistances to be met by the power generated by an engine. Trucks had to be served at Studebaker as well as automobiles. With the aid of his staff, Sparrow kept after the facts, and added them up to the best solutions.

All features of a car are important. But when the depres-

sion during Sparrow's first decade with Studebaker forced
so many people to use cars longer, service and durability
of a car's engine increased in importance. Conditions in
the economic world brought oblivion to some automobile
concerns, reorganization and consolidations to others. Hundreds of companies had appeared and disappeared when,
finally, the whole passenger car industry in the United
States was left in the hands of fewer than a dozen companies. Studebaker was one of these companies, and part
of the reason for it was an engineer, name of Sparrow, who
was by this time recognized as one of the industry's top-
flight engine and research experts. He had been named
head of his company's research department when a vacancy
gave opportunity for the promotion. As administrative and
personnel duties fell to him he proved adept at developing
other good halfbacks to carry the ball. Without interfering
with their work in the slightest he could look at his team's
problems and state the facts with an uncanny clarity that
revealed clues and spurred a man to move on under his own
steam.

Then World War II arrived, with grim reality for our
own country, and conditions in the automobile field
changed. Rapid airplane production was of paramount importance; automobile companies turned their facilities over
for the manufacture of airplane parts. The Studebaker
Corporation entered upon a five-year project to manufacture the Wright-Cyclone engine, and upon Mr. Sparrow
would fall full responsibility for production testing of these
engines, failure of any one of which might mean calamity
to a group of our best flying men.

It was many months before engines were ready to test
but the time was none too long for the preparation of the
extensive test facilities required. These eventually included
one of the largest banks of test cells in the industry, together with special cells for "Type" tests. Equipment had

to be provided for tests of accessories as well as of engines and the most careful precaution had to be taken against accidents. Gasoline is always a hazard and gasoline had to be used in enormous quantities. Most important of all, the personnel had to be trained and this personnel, for the most part, included people who were without previous experience in this type of work. There were a multitude of things to be done and when engines were built, staff and equipment were ready to test them.

There is no need to tell here the story of American air power in the latter years of World War II. But several facts may be recorded. First, Studebaker produced a great proportion of the engines that powered our Flying Fortresses. Second, the job exemplified by collaboration between the Wright Aeronautical Corporation and Studebaker could have taken place in no other country in the world because no other country had the degree of standardization to make such speedy collaboration possible. Third, Stan Sparrow was one of the big reasons why the project succeeded as it did.

The time came when automobile companies were able to return to pre-war pursuits and Sparrow returned to his old job with the new title of director of research. But he did not remain long with this title. His work as a research engineer, his demonstrated ability for administrative duties, and his capacity for working with people in ways which brought out their best in work and in human relationships had made him more and more valuable to his company. In 1945 he became vice-president of the Studebaker Corporation in charge of engineering. Another engineer had attained a top-level position in the management of industry, assuming a share of the responsibilities which, in a genuine democracy, every professional group needs to assume in the management of the specific fields of life in which they serve and earn their livings.

Sparrow was to have only seven years in which to carry the responsibilities of his top-level position until an automobile accident would bring a sudden end to his life. In those years he did not confine himself to the job that paid his salary. He served as president of the Society of Automotive Engineers and then took over chairmanship of its Technical Board. In work of this kind, demanding large slices of his time, he aided the automobile and aircraft industries in developing cooperative engineering projects which are of value to industry in peacetime and of value to all the people because they are preparedness for national defense.

For recreation he often clipped along at a good pace between South Bend and Chicago for an evening at the theater. But the thing he enjoyed most was to be able to keep delving and digging away for facts governing internal-combustion engines, and figuring out how to make a better one.

Harold Alden Wheeler

(1903 –   )

RADIO AND TELEVISION ENGINEER WHOSE
TEEN-AGE INVENTION HELPED FINANCE
HIS COLLEGE EDUCATION, AND WHOSE
LATER INVENTIONS HELPED WIN WORLD
WAR II

🔲🔲🔲🔲🔲🔲🔲🔲🔲🔲🔲🔲🔲🔲🔲🔲🔲🔲🔲🔲🔲🔲🔲🔲🔲

THE field of radio and television is one in which clear distinction between scientist and engineer is hard to make. As Harold Alden Wheeler sees it, a degree in physics may be a better starting point today than a degree in engineering for the young man aiming at radio or television engineering, especially if he has qualifications for creative leadership in the field. Mr. Wheeler began to supervise the work of other young radio engineers when he was far from a graybeard himself; he has often found that the young man who enters the field with only four years of college work is better prepared for many jobs if those years have led to a B.S. in physics. A glance through the list of Fellows of the Institute of Radio Engineers indicates how often the undergraduate work of the individuals in this group was directed toward a B.S. in physics, as Mr. Wheeler's was.

It is true that engineering schools may cover this field of the sciences as adequately in preparing a young man for a B.S. in electrical engineering as other institutions may in preparing them for a B.S. in physics. Much depends upon the institution. In general, young men entering radio or television engineering today seem to be coming from science courses in non-specialized colleges as often as from the engineering colleges. Those who do come from the engineering colleges have usually chosen the communications or electronics course, within the department of electrical engineering.

Harold Wheeler was one of those fortunate young men who waste no time wondering what their lifework is to be. Before he entered eighth grade he had made up his mind not just to study science and technology but to be a consulting engineer in "wireless," as radio was then called. That was before America had entered World War I—before more than a handful of such consultants existed. A scientist father who knew nothing about the intricacies of wireless, but a very great deal about how to give intelligent encouragement to a son with a mechanical and scientific bent was partly responsible for a thirteen-year-old boy's comprehension of what being a consulting engineer meant. In fact, Harold Wheeler recognizes that his father was a constructive factor all along the road to his early professional achievement.

"All through life I've had 'good breaks,'" he says, "and having my particular father for a father was the second of my lucky breaks for the work I was to do. The first, of course, was being born with the intellectual equipment which enabled me to go ahead in what I wanted."

Another good break lay in the quality of his early schooling in Mitchell, South Dakota. He had been born, on May 10, 1903, in St. Paul, Minnesota, where his father was teaching agricultural science at the University of Minnesota, but when he was very young, the family moved to the neighboring state. Mitchell, with a population of some nine or ten thousand people, was a community of high living standards—a community where it was customary for people to work hard for what they had, and to support excellent public schools with cultural advantages unusual for communities of its size and location. Harold spent the first seven years of his school life in Mitchell, and his work in seventh grade had been in the hands of a departmentalized staff of four teachers, one of whom taught nothing but music and the arts. When later he entered eighth grade in the public schools of Washington, D.C., he recognized their inferiority to the Mitchell schools. At Chevy Chase, the suburb in which he lived, fifty students in a crowded classroom had one superannuated teacher who served also as school principal, and who was assisted by one itinerant teacher of music and art.

If it is true that New Englanders have been those who first stressed the idea that hard work is a virtue, Harold's parents probably felt at home in Mitchell. They were both of old New England background. His mother, from whom he got his middle name, was an Alden in direct descent from John Alden and Priscilla. The home they made for their children was one in which moral and educational values were stressed, and cultural advantages provided. Harold and his four younger sisters went to public schools during the week and to church and Sunday School on Sunday, and came home to parents who were "undogmatic intelligent liberals, in religion as in everything else," Mr. Wheeler says, no matter what day of the week.

If it is true that talent and interest in the arts is likely to accompany high creative gifts in science and technology, Mr. Wheeler fits this picture, too. As a boy in Mitchell he played the piano so well that he was encouraged by one of his teachers to make music his career. He still plays the piano for his own pleasure but now "the flesh is weak," he says, when it comes to the technique.

Mechanical, and eventually electrical apparatus held a stronger attraction for Harold than did his piano, and he was fortunate in his parents' response. He had all the books and magazines, erector sets and mechanical apparatus he needed.

"The grocery bills waited sometimes, as I remember it," he says, "but especially after my father saw that a twelve-year-old boy was understanding things he did not understand himself, he never allowed temporary money shortages to prevent me from having equipment I needed. His own master's degree in science had given him a pretty good foundation in physics, and he had admiration for whatever it was that enabled me to grasp things which were beyond him."

Harold had not progressed as far as experiments in radio when he left Mitchell. He had kept busy on the type of experiments which came naturally before radio and for which his appetite was whetted by popular lecturers who came to the community each winter. He distinctly remembers hearing lectures on liquid air, on the gyroscope, on "spark wireless," and ultra-violet light. "I used to eat those lectures up and go home and do more experiments," he recalls. Older boys in Mitchell were already working at radio and he knew what he wanted to do and was moving up to that stage when his father accepted a position as a scientist on the staff of the U.S. Department of Agriculture. Harold and a chum who lived on the next block were seriously discussing which type of communication, telegraph or radio, they were going to establish between their homes, but had not yet come to their decision when the Wheeler family moved to Washington.

For all of Mitchell's educational advantages, Washington's museums and libraries were a wonderful new experi-

ence for Harold that first summer in Washington. It was
hot and humid—the kind of heat with which he had not
had experience. But it was not hot enough to wilt a thirteen-year-old's enthusiasm about what he was seeing.

His next breaks were already in the making when the
Wheelers arrived in Washington. The family as yet owned
no automobile but the house they rented in Chevy Chase
had a garage. This gave Harold a full-size workshop. Also,
Washington's first modern high school was being built and
would be completed in time for him to enter it upon completion of eighth grade. "Central High" had modern machine shop equipment, a gymnasium, a swimming pool and,
most important of all, an excellent teaching staff. It also
had a compulsory activity, the High School Cadet Corps,
which Mr. Wheeler looks back upon as a most valuable
experience. He had grown into habits which kept him
indoors with little physical exercise. During his four high
school years he had to drill twice a week with the Cadets,
usually out of doors on the city's streets. The discipline,
the sheer physical exertion, and the daily hours of fresh air
improved both his posture and his health.

"I never rated high militarily," he admits, "but that experience was a very good thing for me. Since I was never
interested in athletics, the compulsory feature of the Cadet
Corps was another break for me. If I had been given the
privilege of choice I probably would not have chosen it,
certainly not four years of it."

Though he did not rate high militarily in his high school
years he rated high enough scholastically. If he did not
stand at the very top of his class, it was probably because
he felt no need to. He was always willing to snatch time
from his homework for his workshop. His day began frequently at 6 A.M. with an hour in the shop before break-
fast. Afternoon school periods were followed by cadet
drill which meant marching for an hour or two, so it was

often dinner time when he got home. After dinner he began his homework. Within an hour, often less, he was too sleepy for study; then he went to bed so he could be up by six next morning.

During his third year in high school he passed government examinations, with a mark of one hundred per cent on the theory, and received a commercial radio operator's license. This permitted him to set up and operate an amateur radio station. He was never interested in using his station for sending messages, but rather in testing and rebuilding the equipment over and over. Would it work if he did this? What would happen if he did that? His interest lay in what made Station 3QK work, and why!

In his senior year he took time off to learn to dance, a recreation he still enjoys along with ping pong and Chinese checkers. Occasional time was still being found for playing the piano. With all of this, standing first or second in his class seemed of secondary importance.

It did seem important, though, for him to win a scholarship to George Washington University. Seven scholarships, each covering tuition for four years of college work, were available each year to Central High seniors who made the seven highest grades in competitive examinations. Nothing helped here but good marks. Harold ranked third the year he took the examinations. In similar examinations later, he notes with a little pride, one of his four sisters stood second and another first.

He had taken the pre-engineering course in high school and now elected the physics course at George Washington as his best preparation for the radio field.

"My next break was a physics professor who was a 'radio bug,'" he says. "When Dr. Thomas B. Brown discovered my work and interest in radio, he helped me in every way he could. There was nothing regimented about my college course. I was permitted to take postgraduate courses in physics in my undergraduate days and I was given all kinds of freedom in the college laboratories."

The curriculum he chose was rich in mathematics and physics, and even in radio. He graduated at the top of his class with the honor of valedictorian and the award of the Ruggles Medal in Mathematics.

Good reasons for his curricular freedoms are apparent in certain facts of Wheeler's life during his college days. The summer before he entered college, and the following summer, he had a job at the U.S. Bureau of Standards where three small radio laboratories had recently been established. Some of the master minds of radio were in and out of these laboratories constantly and young Wheeler had opportunity to meet and talk and even work with these men. Commercial broadcasting was in its infancy and one of the troublesome problems being talked about was "How can the squeals be taken out of radio?" Through his work at the Bureau of Standards the still teen-age Wheeler recognized need for an improvement in amplifiers which could be effective in solving this problem, and began to have ideas of his own along this line.

The summer following his freshman year in college he incorporated his ideas in a type of circuit which would later become known as the Neutrodyne circuit. It was very crude as he set it up, but it worked.

At this point Harold's story stops a moment for his father's. Mr. W. A. Wheeler, through interest in developing his son's talents, had become alert to the usefulness of radio and had instituted radio reports in the Department of Agriculture. For that reason he was now sitting as his Department's representative on the Hoover radio committee set up by the Department of Commerce. On this committee were some of the best known scientists and technologists in the radio world.

Shortly after Harold had completed his crude neutralizing circuit, he made a trip with his father to New York. Lunching with a friend in the Delaware and Lackawanna Station at Hoboken, they ran into Professor Alan Hazeltine from near-by Stevens Institute of Technology, a member of the Commerce Department's committee and hence an acquaintance of the elder Mr. Wheeler. Hazeltine came over to the table where the Wheelers were seated. Mr. Wheeler introduced his son and Hazeltine said as he left, "Stop in and see me when you're finished."

The invitation was accepted and within five minutes of the time the two Wheelers entered Professor Hazeltine's office they had discovered that Hazeltine was at that moment building a Neutrodyne set containing the essential feature of the one Harold had set up, and had plans on paper in a patent application filed in the U.S. Patent Office.

"Does it work?" Hazeltine wanted to know about the crude set in Washington, and Harold assured him that it did.

There were perhaps a half dozen researchers in the country, working on this same idea at that time, and two of them discovered each other by accidental meeting that afternoon in Hoboken! The results are written into radio history as well as in Harold Wheeler's personal history. Hazeltine's Neutrodyne set came into great popularity, and the Hazeltine Corporation was organized. His patent was granted and he extended an agreement assigning a small share of the royalties to Harold Wheeler. Wheeler's summer jobs were assured for the rest of his college days. The first summer after he met Professor Hazeltine he had the privilege of working with him personally. "That is where I really got my start in radio," he says. "It was a wonderful opportunity to work with a man like that—one of the biggest breaks that ever came my way."

With the organization of the Hazeltine Corporation, Wheeler was put on its staff as a radio engineer with a retaining fee that saw him through his last two years at George Washington, where his scholarship still covered his tuition, and three years of fulltime graduate work in physics at Johns Hopkins University in Baltimore. He went up to Hoboken for a couple of days every month but worked for the most part at the University laboratories or in his own workshop. Before his Johns Hopkins days were over he had married and was supporting a wife and child. Actually, while he had still been a junior at George Washington he had all but attained his goal of being a consulting engineer in "wireless." Certainly in his Johns Hopkins years he was acting as a consultant though his official title with the Hazeltine Corporation would not be that until later.

Wheeler did not take his Ph.D. in physics at Johns Hopkins. His three years of fulltime work would have given him that, had he accepted prescribed procedure for a doctorate. He wanted other things more than he wanted the doctorate and he followed his own desires. Frankly, he does not recommend this path for others. Though lack of the advanced degree has not stood in his way, he advises young men interested in radio and television engineering to work for a Ph.D. if they have capacity and opportunity for work in a graduate school.

His own case, possibly, was enough out of the ordinary to account for and justify his own refusal to bend his interests to meet Johns Hopkins' requirements. Earning his retaining fee from the Hazeltine Corporation was keeping him in touch with radio's practical problems, and studying at Hopkins stressed theory and research in pure science. Wheeler himself had always felt an innate need to "make things work." Engineering has sometimes been defined as the "practical application of the discoveries of science," and by that definition Wheeler, though now a student of advanced science, was still definitely engaged in engineering. His mind had the capacity for advanced scientific theory, but his gifts called strongly toward practical application of theory in a new and rapidly developing field of technology.

During his first Christmas vacation as a graduate student of science (December 1925) he achieved something of technological and practical importance. In his home workshop he built one of the first radio sets ever to be equipped with automatic volume control. It achieved about the same loudness from local and from distant stations without adjusting a volume control knob. That set stands today as the forerunner of the present diode-type automatic volume control (AVC) used on all home radios. Four years after Wheeler had built his first set, working in the Hazeltine laboratory, he designed, and Philco put on the market "the set that put 'AVC' on the map."

Under his working agreement, patents for Wheeler's inventions were in his name but were owned by the Hazeltine Corporation. His AVC patent became one of the many commercially valuable patents in the United States to be beset by years of expensive litigation. Other radio laboratories had been working along similar AVC lines but for ten years some favorable court decisions on Wheeler's priority gave great benefits to the Hazeltine group. Later the Supreme Court handed down an adverse decision which made collection of royalties no longer possible, but could not destroy the priority of Wheeler's set, built when he was only twenty-two.

The type of professional achievement Wheeler had attained during his college days, and then again at the beginning of his postgraduate years, makes it understandable how his own interests impelled him to rate a Ph.D. as of secondary importance, just as standing first in his high school class had seemed unimportant. He had proved so much more about his abilities than had most young men of his age. He had a job waiting which did not depend upon a degree and which offered unusual opportunity. In fact, only two years after he left graduate school, a new Hazeltine research laboratory was organized in Bayside, Long Island, and Wheeler was put in charge of it with great freedom in his work.

Soon he found himself working in television as well as in radio. Actually, Mr. Wheeler says, there is little similarity in the sciences of sound radio and television, but "They grew up together." Each is now a subdivision of what modern colleges call "communications," a word which means in the engineering world the transference of messages either over wires or by the action of waves operating in the atmosphere or ether. In the early 1930's—still a pre-television period—men were moving naturally from the earlier communications field to the emerging field of television. In that decade Wheeler became a recognized specialist in both fields, an achievement not so likely to happen now because of the extreme specialization required since television has entered a higher stage of development. While at Johns Hopkins, he had published his first important technical paper, and it had to do with a subject which would become as important in television as it was in radio— wave filters. Filters and tuners are still among his specialties.

His years at the Bayside Laboratory, before war needs directed his work into newer channels, were years of fulfillment and technical achievement. A discussion of the work of those years would be largely unintelligible to the layman, but a few facts give an idea about its volume, variety, and quality. By 1940 Wheeler had received the Modern Pioneer Award of the National Association of Manufacturers in recognition of more than one hundred patents in his name. (The number had risen to more than one hundred and fifty by 1951.) He had also received the Morris Liebmann Prize of the Institute of Radio Engineers "for contribution to the analysis of wide-band, high-frequency circuits particularly suitable to television." His work had aided in the solution of distortion problems in television as it had aided earlier in diminishing sound distortions in radio. It had been recognized in the scientific world by election as a Fellow of both the Institute of Radio Engineers and the American Institute of Electrical Engineers. Nearer home it had been recognized by his being named vice-president of the Hazeltine Electronics Corporation and its chief consulting engineer.

World War II took Wheeler away from television. The whole Hazeltine Corporation became part of a joint effort, entered into by scientists, engineers, and manufacturing concerns, to invent, develop, and produce devices which would win the war. Much of the scientific work done in American laboratories for the Government is still secret and Wheeler still works mainly on secret projects which cannot be written about. One of the things no longer secret is the information that the Hazeltine Corporation engineered the "Interrogation-Friend-or-Foe" (IFF) equipment attached to all radar sets on the ground, on ships and on aircraft in the latter years of the war. This equipment permitted the radar operator to push a button and read on his indicating instrument the answer to whether an approaching plane or ship was one of "ours" or one of "theirs." Wheeler's continuous effort and his contributions to this project were recognized by the "Certificate of Commendation for outstanding service to the United States Navy during World War II."

Another thing which is not secret is that Wheeler himself was in charge of the design of the one mine detector used by the army to locate buried mines. Pictures of men using the detector were widely published in the war reports. The portable equipment included a circular "paddle" containing a set of coils. It was carried on a long handle so it could be swept from side to side ahead of the soldier using it. The presence of a buried mine was indicated by a shrill tone when the paddle was over the mine. Then it could be dug up and destroyed before it might be detonated by this soldier or his comrades. The first models saw service on Africa's desert and beaches. Production models saw much service in the European campaigns and were widely used by French farmers before plowing their fields after the war.

The war ended in 1945 but the world was in a state of unrest and tension which meant that scientific and technological research, and the development of offensive and defensive equipment and devices would continue. Because of this, Wheeler would have to postpone his return to television. But the end of the war left him free to make one change he had decided on. In 1946 he established his own laboratories in Great Neck, Long Island, where he began to create an environment in which he could put into practice certain ideals he had about working relationships among engineers.

In the main, the ideal Wheeler had in mind was a laboratory where engineers would work for and with other engineers. It seemed to him that when a non-engineer executive was in a position to make demands on engineers who worked *for* him, not *with* him, he was likely to insist on premature answers to problems which would have profited most by the thoughtful analysis which is the genuine engineering approach. Wheeler recognized that expediency must sometimes govern a decision, but to put pressure constantly on engineers for expedient solutions is to poison the wellsprings of their constructive initiative and reduce them to the level of tinkerers. And he had seen more tinkering during the war years than seemed beneficial to progress.

To set up a small laboratory in a field like radio and

television was quite a venture. Expensive equipment is needed. The success of his inventions under Hazeltine's ownership had given him some financial leeway, and he took the steps that brought the Wheeler Laboratories into existence. He could be certain that his own services as a consultant would be in demand, no matter where he had his offices, and these could take care of his family responsibilities. The Laboratories might risk his capital but not his professional capacity to earn. It soon became evident that the financial risks were well worth while. Research of significance to America's post-war defense efforts has taken place in Wheeler Laboratories, whose services have been in demand from the beginning. This is also true of Wheeler's personal services as consulting radio physicist, which are utilized by various companies and by the Government in his capacity as one of the expert consultants attached to the Office of the Secretary of Defense.

Working with Bell Telephone Laboratories, the newly organized Wheeler Laboratories designed the complicated microwave circuits in the heart of the tracking radar that guides the Nike missile to its aircraft target. Their more recent work in the field of radar and guided missiles is still under secrecy restrictions. They are now actively contributing to the design of the world's largest radio transmitter which the Navy is constructing in Maine for communication with submerged submarines.

In 1957 the facilities of Wheeler Laboratories were doubled by the addition of a new antenna laboratory with a testing range at Smithtown, further out on Long Island. The staff was increased to about thirty engineers while the objective remains the same. Here is a laboratory in which engineers will work for and with other engineers. The environment will remain one in which each engineer's advice will be solicited, will always be appreciated, and will often be followed. Expediency may be accepted as necessary at times, but to seek understanding of a problem will always be recognized as genuine economy in engineering.

If respect for hard work and high standards of living were a mark that Mitchell, South Dakota, left on Harold Wheeler in youth, he has carried its mark back almost to the New England of his forefathers. His Long Island home life today is based upon the same fundamentals he grew up with in his parents' home. Life is distinctly of the age in which it is being lived, but standards are high and fundamental values are of more importance than keeping up with the Joneses. Wheeler works hard and finds time out of hours for the preparation of still more technical papers which are clear and concise.

"That was another of my lucky breaks," he says, "the fact that certain types of writing came easy to me. I did not like English in high school or pay much attention to it in college. I never put much effort on it anywhere. This would have stood in my way if I had not had some small talent in expressing factual material in writing. The engineer who wants to 'go places' in his professional life needs to learn how to write good clear English, and he should see to it that he learns to do this early—in high school or college."

Wheeler has respect for his work but he sees his life as greatly blessed by good breaks. The outsider looking at it is impressed by the fact that what he calls his breaks were matters which might have meant nothing to many young men. Good breaks gave him opportunity to forge ahead because he was ready to work to use them. Admittedly they helped him achieve earlier than he might otherwise have done. But Harold Wheeler has forged ahead through his own work and effort, and the aim of the Wheeler Laboratories is to make it possible for other engineers to do the same.